Thank you
for being part of it!

You can go one step further
by signing up for the newsletter
or buying further copies on:
www.carbonbuddyproject.org

There are also several more ways
you can get involved. Take a quick
peek at page 77 for other ideas!

Many thanks again

Colin Hastings
aka
**#mycarbonbuddy**

# To our future generations.

To my wife Helen (the first Carbon Buddy) for her patience, her support and her significant contribution to this book.

To my sons Nick and Matt, whose loving flattery helped me to keep going.

To our grandchildren, Toby, Rosie and Sophie, their future and their children's future.

To our friends' grandchildren, their future and their children's future.

To those future generations that you, the reader and user of this manual, will hold in mind as you read about and become part of this massive project. I invite you to write their names here:

www.carbonbuddyproject.org

Business as usual
Cool planet

Published by The Carbon Buddy Project

PO Box 789, TRURO, Cornwall, TR1 9LQ, UK

To find out more about the Carbon Buddy Project, visit:

**carbonbuddyproject.org**

First published March 2020
Second edition November 2020

ISBN 978-1-916282-71-1



A catalogue record for this book is available from The British Library.



Book Design by Austin Taylor
www.bookdesigner.co.uk

Edited by Caroline Petherick
https://the-wordsmith.co.uk

Branding and website by Design Room Cornwall
https://www.designroomcornwall.com

Print on Demand by Ingram Spark

# The Carbon Buddy Manual

## Your practical guide to cooling our planet

COLIN HASTINGS

#mycarbonbuddy

# Contents

# Acknowledgements

## To all those who have helped shape the Carbon Buddy Project

I didn't really set out to write this manual. The seed just blew in from somewhere, a place both within and without. There came a point when this seed demanded to be sown. Fortunately, a mixture of events, ideas and a wide range of people played their parts in bringing this small seed to life, to get it started. Fortunately, there were further events and people who appeared at the right times to feed it and nurture it through times of doubt and drought. Lack of space means that I can't give thanks to everyone. More are listed on the carbonbuddyproject.org website. **Thank you all.**

*See box on page 13 for details*

### The seeds

- My wife, Helen, who read about the IPCC (Intergovernmental Panel on Climate Change) Report SR15 in October 2018 while I was away cycling in Italy, and said, 'We've done a lot, but it's not enough. We have to do much more.'
- My colleagues from way back – Julia Pokora, Wendy Briner, Mike Geddes and Frank Tyrrell – who helped to shape a range of ideas about teamworking and organisational change which appear here in disguise.
- My son, Matt, who studied Environmental Resource Management and who told me, amongst many other things, how I could measure our carbon footprint.
- Professor Richard Cochrane, who organised a climate change conference at Falmouth University where I heard a talk by Stephan Harrison and came across *Drawdown*. They expected 40 people. 250 turned up.
- Giuliana Hanman, our Italian teacher, who suggested that Helen and I should make a climate change presentation to the class. The class were very kind in their response. Giuliana was also kind enough to read and comment on an early draft. ***Grazie a tutti.***
- Greta Thunberg, who has impressed me hugely with her courage and the wonderful clarity and directness of her speaking which I could only dream of emulating.

*You must be the change you wish to see in the world.*

MAHATMA GANDHI


## Feeding and nurturing

Three friends – Jane Turnbull, John Brown and Ian Grant – played significant roles in helping me to navigate my way through the world of publishing. Dianne Stadhams and Annie Friedlein provided further encouragement.

Helen Hart at SilverWood Books, who was very generous with her time and advice.

## Growing

Several people at CAT, the Centre for Alternative Technology, have helped to support and shape the Carbon Buddy Project and this manual. Thanks so much to Eileen Kinsman, Tanya Hawkes, and Joel Rawson in particular.

I am also grateful for very constructive and useful feedback from delegates at the CAT conference in 2019 who attended my workshop. Special thanks to Gemma Hurst for volunteering to be the first Carbon Buddy Propagator.

Henry Rising at Hawksmoor Investment Management who, with his colleagues, rose to my challenges about carbon reduction investment.

Ben Coles and Michelle Balfour from Cascadia Author Services in Canada have provided expert support and know-how in helping me to navigate through the complexities of setting up this second edition for Print on Demand which means it will be available online internationally. My sincere thanks to them.

## Harvesting

Andy Vosper at TJ International, who so generously gave me a fascinating and absorbing master class in book printing.

Caroline Petherick, who has crisped up my writing no end, and has done so much more than editing by being both knowledgeable about the subject and enthusiastic about the whole project.

A team of young talented creatives to help me with the self-publishing process, who have been a huge source of stimulation, energy and encouragement. Charlie Guidal as marketing and social media consultant was the first; we worked together on the strategy and to bring in Emma Gordon and Sally Mitchell (branding and website) and Austin Taylor (book design). Subsequently Ellie Mason joined the team to boost our social media visibility and run special campaigns, whilst Issy Dean joined as a research volunteer and representative of GenZ.

And finally, Sophia Hetherington who responded to an SOS and took on all the organising of speaking events and databases, and a myriad other detailed tasks, thus helping considerably to preserve my sanity.

CHAPTER 1

▶ Think of this manual as a *toolkit for getting started* (and keeping going)

▶ Think of this manual as a *process of discovery*

▶ Think of this manual not as a book to be read but as a *book to be used*

INTRODUCTION

# ▶ What to expect

You've probably registered already that this is not a normal climate change book. I like to refer to it as a manual. And I see the manual taking us on a low carbon ride (on a bike, a boat, a train? You choose.) And we're all going on it together. Let me try to give you a flavour of what might be in store.

## Join me on the ride

I'm going on my folding bike! She's called Brava, and I've done some interesting slow travel rides with her. This ride, however, promises to be particularly interesting and stimulating. But it won't be fast, and it won't always be comfortable. At times it'll be bumpy, but we'll get through by working and sticking together. There's going to be a lot of fun too. Some of that will come from the many interesting characters we'll meet along the way.

## Simple, but not simplistic

- I want this to be **a practical 'how to' guide for practical 'how to' people.**
- It's not just for reading, though. You'll see sections where you'll be able to write ... and even paint or draw! Think of it as a workbook.
- I want to write it as far as possible without jargon, and to be clear and simple to follow. Most pages will be shorter than this one.
- This means that it can't contain all the answers to questions that you may want answered.
- To solve this, and to ensure that information in this fast-changing field is up to date, this manual is backed up by **carbonbuddyproject.org.** Here you will find specific links to all sorts of further information on topics in the manual. No more endless searching on the web or in weighty books!

# Warming up

**If you're itching to get going,** and want to take the fast track, I suggest you jump to Chapter 4 on page 36. There you can dive straight into looking at your carbon footprint. But come back here afterwards! This section will prepare you for your next steps.

## Bite-size chunks

- Climate change is a huge and complex subject. I've tried to break it down into bite-size chunks to make it feel more manageable. You'll gradually discover the 19 steps that you can take at your own pace. You don't have to do them in order, though I would suggest you start with the first six.
- And when it comes to planning what you have decided to do, the manual will help you break it down into manageable chunks spread over a reasonable period of time.
- You'll also come across the nudge boxes sprinkled throughout the manual. These are little thought starters.

## Advice?

- I'm not convinced that advice is always helpful. One of my professors years ago used to say: 'Help strikes again!'
- Even if I was an expert (which I'm not) I would steer clear of giving advice – ie telling you what you should do. I can't know your situation. Instead I've tried to offer options and ideas, and occasional insights from my own experience.
- Then you can weigh up what you have found out from me and from your Carbon Buddy (for more, read on!), from other sources on the website, and from people you meet.
- And then make your decisions. Only you know what's going to work for you.

dig deeper www.

*Show me where the hope is, and then I'll do something.*

STRANGER IN THE SUPERMARKET

## Optimism and hope

- It's a positive story. The solutions are clear. We need to mobilise huge numbers of people to do stuff. And that means all sorts of people. There is something for you in this manual, whether you're well off or not. I believe that everyone has resources which can help. **The manual concentrates on what you have, not on what you don't have.**
- At the heart of the ride lies the idea of having a Carbon Buddy as your travel companion. And it's based on friendship, the simple power of face-to-face relationships, respect, cooperation, and common purpose. Idealistic? No. It just works. Trying to do this ride alone is too much for most of us.
- I've built in a few psychological tips to keep you motivated for the long haul.

## The power of reflection

Although this manual is primarily about getting on and doing things, that does need to be balanced by periods of reflection. **It's a bit like stopping on the ride to admire the view.** In the reflective periods you often discover a new perspective. Similarly, in this book I'm suggesting using different methods to reflect:

- Discover your inner artist: draw, colour, paint pictures. Express yourself with images rather than words.
- Take stock: take time to review what you've decided, and put it into a coherent plan.
- Think about change: spend some time in musing about the psychology of behaviour change.
- Walk away and come back later: very helpful if you're feeling stuck or frustrated.

## A quiet sense of purpose

- I used to be a management psychologist. My professional life was all about creating high-performing teams. There are some who believe that individuals can't solve big problems. But I know from my background that motivated individuals working together towards a very clear objective **can achieve what seems to be the impossible.**
- I'll be asking you to take a role in building the wider Carbon Buddy Community, a growing network of individuals with the same objective. It will involve relatively little effort. You can be a catalyst to help it take off.

## Equally important, though, is what it's NOT

- It's not about lots of meetings, big egos, arguments, being lectured at, street protests, ridicule, shame, accusations, blame, feeling stupid or inadequate.
- It's not driven by academic rigour or waiting until we have the right answer. Instead it's driven by a practical imperative. It's about getting on and doing what seems reasonable and good enough, given what we think we know at the moment. Action is needed **now.**

## And finally

- The Carbon Buddy Project is my personal investment in trying to help solve what I regard as the biggest problem ever faced by humanity. My payback will be what people like you **do.**

I can provide the spark, and you'll provide the flame.

# Nudge boxes

As you work your way through this manual, you'll frequently come across little boxes in the margins of the pages. Each of these is a different kind of invitation. Cumulatively, they will help you (and your brain!) to think, imagine, discover and put together the many elements which will finally become your carbon reduction plan, tailored to your own personal circumstances. Each different kind of nudge box has its own icon and colour so that they will be instantly recognisable.

| | | |
|---|---|---|
| **Seeds of hope** | **Look out for** the positive stuff. It's there and there's more and more of it. Here's where to record and celebrate the seeds of the emerging low-fossil-fuel-future. | SEEDS OF HOPE |
| **How About?** | **Consider** these action ideas which are sprinkled throughout the manual (normal lists can be so tedious!). Some will be easy, some will challenge you, all deserve to be listened to. | HOW ABOUT? |
| **Dig deeper** | **Refer to carbonbuddyproject.org.** Here you will find additional links carefully selected to give you more information on the specific topic you're working on. | dig deeper www. |

# Is it all pessimistic?

In some ways it is. There are very real and present signs of a climate crisis, whether or not we choose to believe that humans have contributed to it. Here's a poignant example:

## A letter to the future

'Ok' is the first Icelandic glacier to lose its status as a glacier.

In the next 200 years all our glaciers are expected to follow the same path.

This monument is to acknowledge that we know what is happening and what needs to be done.

Only you know if we did it.

AUGUST 2019

*415 ppm $CO_2$*

HOW ABOUT?

**Putting** a notice near your shower saying 'stop dreaming'

Plaque to commemorate the first death of an Icelandic glacier, called Ok.

English version of an epitaph written by an Icelander, Andri Snær Magnason

# No it's not!

## Another letter to the future

There are many grounds for optimism. There are proven solutions aplenty.

The exciting challenge is to roll those out rapidly ...

... and to grow the number of people actively involved exponentially ...

... and to do those things that will make the biggest difference quickly

Simple!

Read on to find out how to play an active part in the most important, challenging and exciting collective rescue effort of all time.

HOW ABOUT?

**Gradually** changing over all your garden machinery to mains (green) electric or battery power.

INTRODUCTION

# The physics is clear enough

## Uncomfortable listening

I have over time become convinced that climate change is real and requires us to respond. When my son, who knows a lot about these things, says he is scared for his children, I have to listen. When I go and hear a top physicist speak passionately about the uncomfortable conclusions that he has had to draw, I have to listen. It all makes for uncomfortable listening. But for me that's not a reason *not* to listen. My challenge is to find a way to respond. And that's uncomfortable too.

## An 'aha!' moment: the nature and scale of the challenge

Stephan Harrison's talk at a conference at my local university was one of the catalytic events that set me on the path to writing this manual. Here's a brief summary of his core conclusions:

> *The physics is clear. Climate change impacts are real, destructive and on the increase. But the symptoms are not uniform around the globe. They take different forms in different places. Furthermore, climate change is accelerating alarmingly, and is wreaking havoc now, especially in parts of the world that are not on our euro-centric radar. We don't see the half of it.*
>
> *The consequences of our lifestyles here produce tangible effects there. The consequences of what is happening there will affect us here. And saying that 'there' has to take all the mitigating action misunderstands how the physics and the world is interconnected. Action has to be taken everywhere.*

# The bigger picture



But most importantly, action has to be ramped up to **a scale hitherto unimaginable** to make sufficient difference in the very short time before it becomes irreversible.

**Ohmigod.** What happens if you have somehow started reading this book and you don't believe the physics?

It's not a problem for me. But for you it may present a dilemma: *What do I do with this damn manual?*

Here are three suggestions, for what they're worth:

- Chuck the book away (an awful waste of all that FSC paper)
- Give it to a friend
- Hang in a bit longer and see if you get a pleasant surprise or two. You never know ...

# And so are the goals

## SOS (• • • — — — • • •)

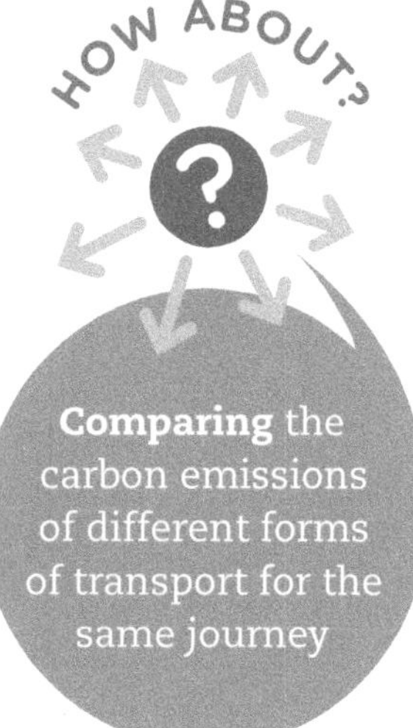


There's quite a lot of confused thinking when it comes to talking about the goals of climate action. Some talk about preserving biodiversity. Others talk about plastic. Yet others will want to focus on clean air, oceans, trees or waste. I tend to see most of these as climate change symptoms or consequences rather than causes. We have to focus on the *root causes, the warming of the earth's atmosphere resulting from the cumulative impact of greenhouse gas emissions which result from our fossil fuel-dependent lifestyles.*

I also worry about another widely used definition of the goal. We hear the phrase SAVING THE PLANET time and time again. To me, it's quite clear that the planet will be fine. It will still exist, though not as we know it. What won't exist is humanity as we know it. So the goal we are actually talking about is 'saving our selves' (the origin of the international distress call SOS!). And that means weaning us off our fossil fuel-dependent lifestyles.

## The big picture: humanity's collective goal

Our goal is to leave behind a habitable planet for all current and future generations

In the short to medium term that means a planet that is cooling, not warming. So I call this:

**Our Cool Planet Goal**

## Personal goals for individuals and households

I've already described briefly the massive challenge that global warming throws at us. It requires us both to *scale up and to speed up our human response in a way hitherto unimaginable*. But how do you translate that daunting challenge into practical personal action? How should you describe and focus your personal response so that it lies within your own control? As a friend of mine once remarked 'if you don't know where you're going, you'll probably end up somewhere else!'

Here's what I find gives me focus, resolve and a sense of urgency. I hope it helps you in turn to be crystal clear about your personal response to the climate emergency.

# My personal cool planet goal

## How to make the biggest impact I can in the shortest possible time?

### WHAT DO I MEAN BY IMPACT?

1 CARBON FOOTPRINT: how to make substantial and rapid reductions in my personal pollution.

2 PROPAGATION: how to take responsibility for inspiring and helping at least ten other people to follow my lead.

3 BARRIER BUSTING: how to identify and find ways round any barriers that undermine my, or other people's, carbon reduction ambitions.

# There are proven solutions aplenty

## Another 'aha!' moment: *Drawdown*.

My second big breakthrough was coming across the book *Drawdown*, (see page 116), billed as **'the most comprehensive plan ever proposed to reverse global warming'.** Well, I don't know about you, but that sort of claim normally turns me off. But at that point I was desperate; even though I had skimmed many climate change books, I still lacked a clear view of how we could dig ourselves out of this hole. I was curious, so I dipped into it.

HOW ABOUT?

**Installing** a dehumidifier – with one, you'll feel more comfortable at a lower temperature

The book immediately intrigued me. For a start it had really good pictures, which made a change. But beyond those I discovered a very well-written and clearly laid-out manual about all the solutions that already exist and have been proven to work.

## Solutions at last!

Even better, there was real practical experience and scientific know-how behind the authors' work. They had assembled a vast international team of people who knew about these solutions at first hand. This was not theory. This was practice. This was about what works.

**Some solutions have a bigger and quicker impact than others.**

Even better, once the writers had researched all these solutions in great depth, they were able to draw some broad conclusions about **the degree of impact each might have if deployed systematically around the world.** This led them to rank solutions according to their likely benefits. Ambitious or what! I found those ranking tables seriously useful, because they really helped me to see what kinds of actions would help us make the most substantial and rapid progress towards reaching the Cool Planet Goal. Remember that?

To create a quantum leap in the global reduction and absorption of greenhouse gas emissions ... and to do it rapidly.

## Useful information

*Drawdown* is great. But it has lots of numbers which are very useful but difficult to summarise without oversimplifying or creating misunderstanding, so I've condensed its 240 pages into one. My summary isn't perfect, but it's good enough for our purposes. See it on **carbonbuddyproject.org.**

Meanwhile, here's an even shorter summary, guiding us towards our second major challenge:

How to prioritise those actions which will have the biggest and quickest carbon reduction impact.

## The three big ones

Each of the three broad solution clusters listed here is the sum of several different (though related) solutions, each scored according to its potential impact. These three come out head and shoulders above the rest:

1. Decarbonising the food chain (285)
2. Rolling out renewable energy (241)
3. Protecting and enhancing natural carbon storage (148)

**All** these solutions are our priorities.

Don't worry about what the numbers mean. Please take it from me that they represent a rough measure of the relative carbon reduction potential of each of these solutions. The bigger the number the greater the impact.

The main thing here is that we begin to see a picture of the range of solutions that need to be deployed rapidly. *Drawdown* provides us with an informed rationale for where to place our priorities along the ride. But be clear that even though some solutions have lower numbers and others higher ones, it doesn't mean that we only go for the ones with the higher numbers.

What these numbers do is ensure we don't get overwhelmed by the huge range of things that we **could** do. They help us to become clearer about what we **should** do.

**Joining** a car club instead of having your own car

# But the psychology is a bit more complicated!

## Ostriches, snowpersons and barkers

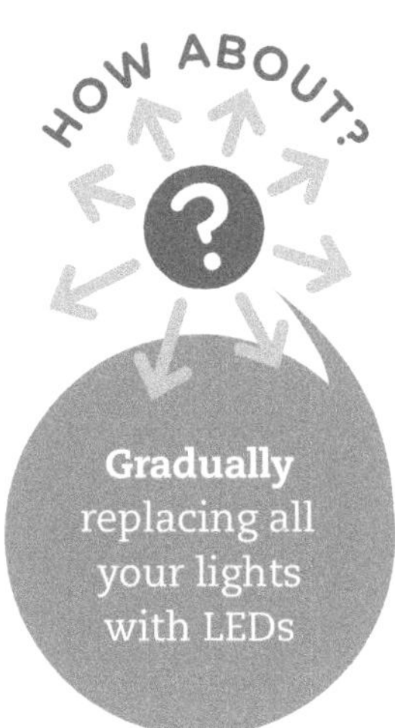


### Fight, flight, freeze

Funny things, humans – we like to think how intelligent, creative, tolerant, and rational we are. And we can be all of those things … until we're threatened. Then our more **fundamental instincts,** derived from our more primitive past, kick in. Faced with an immediate threat, and when we can be clear who or what it is, we either run (flight), attack (fight) or become transfixed (freeze). But it doesn't have to be that way. Those more experienced in dealing with immediate threats react in a very different way, as we shall soon see.

But what if we're warned about threats that seem to be in some far-off country rather than on our home territory? What if those threats appear to be in the distant future? **What if they seem intangible or invisible?** How do we respond to the warnings that we are given about these seemingly remote events?

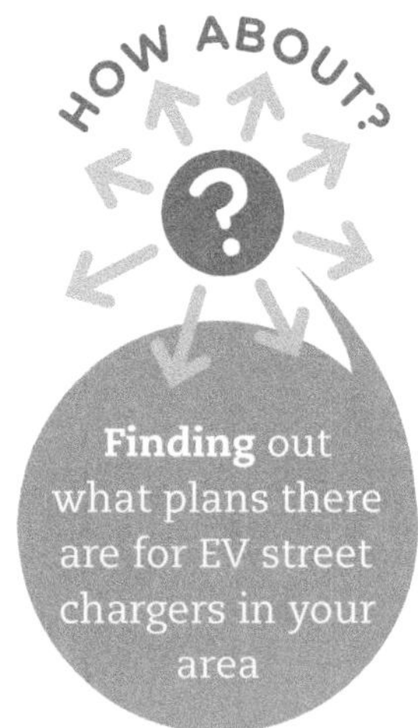


The warnings are uncomfortable psychologically. We have to deal with that discomfort somehow, and the instant response is to try to make them go away – out of thought, out of mind. In this scenario we still use strategies similar to those in the immediate threat scenario, but they take different forms:

**Flight** takes the form of sticking our heads in the sand – the ostrich.

**Fight uses words to attack those who we feel are the enemy,** or to argue endlessly over which approach is the best – barking. (Our modern media landscape has taken barking to a whole new level, leading to many people switching off – another type of ostrich response, I guess.) **Freeze** turns us into a state of helplessness and despair so that action seems impossible – the snowperson.

By making the uncomfortable feelings appear to go away, the ostriches and the barkers end up feeling pretty much OK. Job done. Of course this strategy works fairly well in the short term. But as the threat level changes – as the threat comes ever closer to home and/or becomes more tangible and visible – these folks are not so well prepared.

And the snowpeople are not OK. **They feel stuck.** They may turn to ostrich behaviour or barking as their next best option, but may feel even more uncomfortable with those.

If you find you have these reactions at any time (and who doesn't?) I hope this manual will give you another, and better, way to escape from your misery. **That instinctive discomfort is why we're resistant to warnings.** That's why more and more information about climate change doesn't make us react immediately and positively.

## See it, touch it, feel it

But there are some moments when we **do** seem to swing into action. The most striking one in recent times is perhaps the quantum leap in people's reaction to plastic pollution triggered by David Attenborough's *Blue Planet*. It seems to me that it had this effect for two main reasons. Firstly, it brought this pollution into our living rooms. Although much of it was 'out there', we suddenly noticed that it was 'right here' as well. And the second thing was that we could **see** it. It became something tangible – and by its being tangible, we began to see what we could do about it.

In this manual, we'll be working to try to make our invisible carbon emissions more visible, to bring them from out there to right here, and to focus them on our personal radar screens.

## Feeling helpless

If the pilot of an aeroplane we were in, faced with a loss of engine power and the need to ditch in the sea, were to bark at us or exhibit ostrich or snowperson behaviour, we would rightly be most indignant. If the skipper of a lifeboat were to argue endlessly with the crew about what to do, we would regard that as unprofessional or incompetent. The key thing here of course is that these people have been trained to deal with these threats. They are well prepared.

But none of us has been trained. None of us can be well prepared because we have no past experience to call on. So we are all feeling our way. Perhaps if we can realise and acknowledge that, we can then start to do something about those feelings of helplessness. That recognition can then open the door to us approaching these apparently distant and invisible threats not with fear and inaction, but with curiosity and a calm sense of urgency which looks the threat straight between the eyes, rather than turning our heads away because that makes us feel less uncomfortable.

## Pilot, skipper, rescuer

In creating the Carbon Buddy Project and this manual, I've tried my best to create a way of tackling these huge problems that builds on humankind's main strength – our incredible capacity for working cooperatively to face up to and solve problems – whilst finding ways to reduce or neutralise the negative aspects of fight, flight and freezing which risk incapacitating us just when we are at our most vulnerable. I hope that this **Carbon Buddy Manual will leave you better prepared to be a pilot, a skipper or a rescuer** as we ride together into this uncertain future.

HOW ABOUT?

**Freezing** fresh vegetables in summer for winter consumption

# The power of the rescue

## What we can learn from rescuers?

Rescues captivate us ... Thai kids in caves, earthquake victims, trapped miners, lifeboat rescues, flooded families ... they all touch our hearts and evoke deep feelings. We sense the immediacy of the danger, even from the safety of our sofas. We feel for those in peril. And we wait with tense anticipation as events slowly unfold. We watch the rescuers going about their work, and we feel a sense of joy and relief when they meet with success, intense sadness when they do not. We admire these rescuers. We like to call them heroes. But they wouldn't see themselves as heroes at the time. They're just getting on with a job.

Perhaps that gives all of us some clues about how we should be approaching this threat. If we're really honest with ourselves, we'll know that our behaving like ostriches, barkers or snowpeople won't solve the problems. If instead we observe how these particular people go about their work, I think there are some characteristics of what they do, how they behave, their attitudes and how they go about things, that might come in useful for us as we set off on our ride.

Here's what I've noticed. You will almost certainly be able to add to my list:

1. They are driven by **hope.**
2. They **move calmly** towards the danger.
3. They're **alert** to what might lie ahead.
4. They **assess** the situation carefully and thoroughly.
5. There is **no drama.** They stay calm, measured and focused.
6. They become very clear about their **goals**.
7. They **figure out** what will work.
8. They **plan** meticulously.
9. They **don't rush** into action until they are prepared.
10. But then they **move fast and efficiently.**
11. They **work within a team,** often a small one, but seldom alone.
12. And this helps to give them the strength to be incredibly **tenacious and persistent.**
13. At times they are required by the situations they're facing to show immense **courage.**
14. Paradoxically, though, they are quite **private people.** They don't seek the limelight.

# The biggest rescue project of all time

## Reversing the worst of the damage

Leaving behind a good quality of life for future generations, halting – or better, reversing – the damage caused by our dependency on fossil fuels, rolling out the already proven solutions on a huge scale, mobilising people to act in numbers hitherto unimaginable … all this makes for:

The most exciting and complex collective rescue effort the world has ever had to undertake.

The ambition of the Carbon Buddy Project is not modest. It is to unleash an avalanche of billions of small actions, each fuelled by emotion, positive thinking, creative problem solving, and collaborative working. All this energy needs to be focused, laser-like and with a palpable sense of urgency, on humanity's one shared goal, **to leave behind a habitable planet for all current and future generations.**

It has a unique driver and a compelling purpose. It will be achieved bottom up by legions of ordinary but extraordinary citizens, researchers and entrepreneurs throughout the world working at it themselves, and demanding of governments and big businesses that they too do what is required. Inaction is not an option.

These thoughtful, committed 'doers' are **people like you.**

Quietly powerful.

Be part of it.

Time to get started!

*I'm an 'inactivist': but I do want to DO SOMETHING!*

A FRIEND

# Eight tools for making a difference

Remember this from page 19?

## My personal cool planet goal

### How to make the biggest impact I can in the shortest possible time?

Despite the limitations in our ways of reacting to threats, my starting point is optimistic: to build on our capacity for doing positive things. We **have to** take that view. All other views in my experience result (knowingly or unknowingly) in inaction. **And inaction is not an option.**

**For you there is one simple question.**

And it's NOT
'Can I make an impact??'
but rather
'How will I make an impact?'

Fortunately, we as a species have evolved some sophisticated tools for making a difference. Trouble is, we don't all realise we have these tools, or we know about the tools but don't feel we know how to use them. Well, I not only want to lay out the toolkit clearly so we can all see what we've got, but I also hope to persuade you to have a go at using them. They're not rocket science. And the manual will show you how and where they can be useful.

## Eight tools to make a difference

Detailed answers to that BIG question on the opposite page are peppered throughout this manual and its sister website **carbonbuddyproject.org.** However, to give you a sense of the direction we're riding in, I have some broad answers to guide you:

I can see at least **eight tools** available either to all of us, or many of us, which will enable us to do what we need to do.

These eight tools are:

1 DOING: we can all find aspects of our personal behaviour and lifestyle to change.

2 CAMPAIGNING: we can all find ways of directly putting pressure on governments and businesses (direct campaigning).

3 VOLUNTEERING: we can all volunteer to help in organisations that have the expertise and power to influence (indirect campaigning and lobbying).

4 LEARNING: we can all widen our understanding of the issues and the solutions (good choice: this book is not a bad place to start).

5 DONATING: many of us will be able to find money (according to our means) to donate to organisations that have the expertise and power to influence (indirect campaigning and lobbying).

6 SPENDING: many of us will be able to shift our spending patterns towards products and services that help to reach the Cool Planet Goal.

7 INVESTING: a few of us will be able to provide finance for innovation, production and maintenance of emerging carbon reduction technologies.

8 CREATING: a few of us will see and seize opportunities to create new businesses, social enterprises, arts projects, community groups and other relevant ventures.

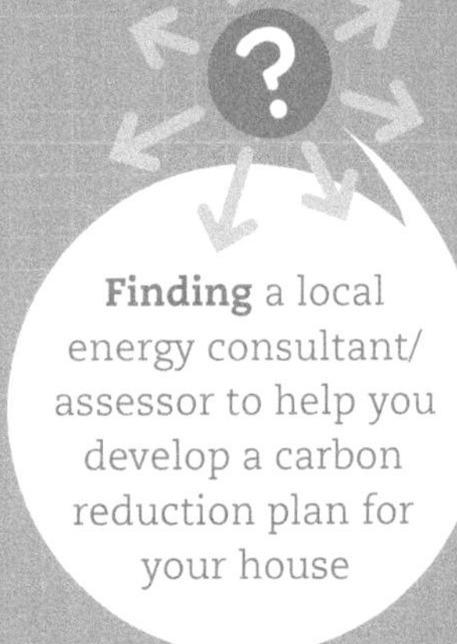


INTRODUCTION

# ▸ Your riding companion

## Don't travel alone

### Two's company

Very few of us are so self-sufficient and so resilient that we can contemplate a long journey by ourselves. But this is what most of us do when we start thinking about responding to climate change. We may not realise quite how big the task is, nor how long it might take. Well, it **is** big and it **will** take quite some time. Why not make it easier for yourself and find a travelling companion? Why not try to turn what could be a solo grind into a fun ride together?

### Introducing your Carbon Buddy

Hence the idea of finding and working with a Carbon Buddy. This simple idea is the throbbing heart of this whole process. It's the idea that doing things together makes them more palatable, more creative, more energising. The idea that a supportive friend can not only help you start, but also help you when you hit roadblocks, and help you when you're distracted or running out of time and energy. In short, help you to keep going. It's a bit like the marathon runner who has pacemakers as running buddies. Except in this race you both win. It's about the power of the pair.

It's all about the power of the pair to motivate each other. Here are a few ideas about how Carbon Buddies can motivate each other:

# Getting started

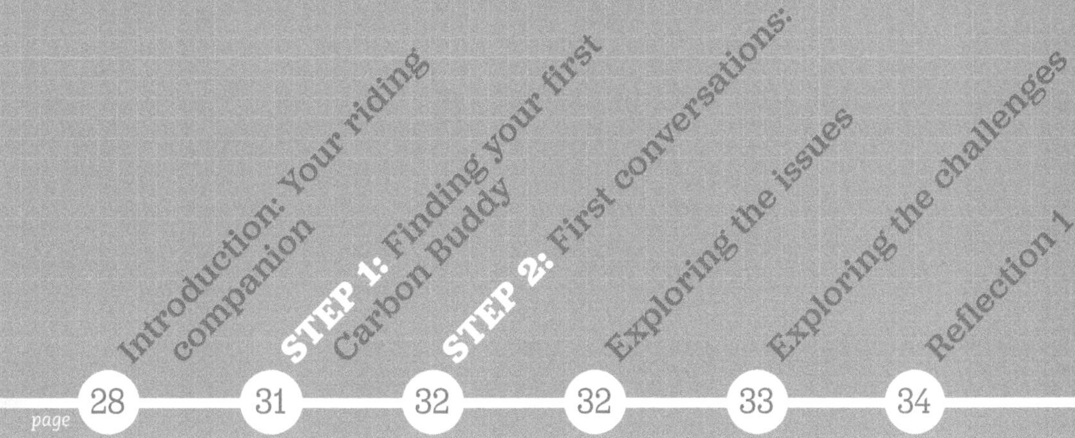


## REWARDS

Dogs love them. Humans need them! There are 20 steps on this ride. It will probably take you a few years to complete. So give yourselves some kind of reward at the end of every step. Each step completed is an excuse for celebration. Only you will know what kind of celebration it will be ... smallish ones for small steps, BIG ones for bigger steps. Who knows? I can only confess that mine tend to have a naughty food element. Pavlova, anyone?

## ACTION PLANNING

On the ride, you'll come across various points where we take stock and do some planning ahead. Planning is not everyone's forte. I probably go over the top a bit. But I commend it to you not only for its practical benefits, but also for its psychological benefits. It gives you an important sense of being in control of a complex process and of knowing where you're going and how far you've gone. This sense of progress, of achievement, is a vital motivational element to help you keep going.

## GENTLE COMPETITION?

As the ride unfolds you'll be coming across more and more other people working to reduce their carbon emissions. A *little* bit of competition can be a good thing. You may not think of yourself as competitive – but maybe there's just a bit of you that wants to do it better than they did! Nevertheless, it's important to recognise and praise their achievements, too. Your recognition will help motivate them, as their recognition will help motivate you.

# Would you be my Carbon Buddy, please?

# STEP 1 Finding your first Carbon Buddy

## Who?

The choice of your first Carbon Buddy is really important. They need to be a good friend, someone you could envisage travelling with or going on holiday with. This idea of strong personal connection is the glue that will hold together the Carbon Buddy Community as it grows. This is the starting point.

There are plenty of places you might look for your first Carbon Buddy. I can see spouses and partners doing it (that was our starting point), families, work colleagues, schoolfriends, neighbours, intergenerational pairs and community groups. I also think about how the more confident can encourage and support the less confident. In particular, having experience of some friends who don't like reading books, and others with dyslexia, working as a pair can help them to get going. It takes the pressure off. It can turn initial caution (sometimes disguised as cynicism) into practical interest, commitment and action.

## Setting off

This of course is not exactly a holiday, though it should turn out to be just as much fun and stimulating, and probably more life-changing. That's the attraction, as is the feeling that together you could join the wider band of Carbon Buddies and make a difference not only in your lives, but more widely.

But don't rush into it. It needs to be a mutual commitment. It needs to matter to you both. Talk through the practical implications for both of you. Are you both prepared to read this book? Are you both prepared and able to give, say, an hour a week to meet in person, on the phone or online?

Also to broach the unthinkable … what happens if it doesn't work for one or both of you? No-blame divorce is the answer. A clean break. Stay friends. Both move on and try again. But let's be optimistic that you'll both continue to feel positive about it.

**ACTION** ZONE

### Simple ground rules for carbon buddies:

- Support each other
- Help each other
- Listen to each other
- Identify the barriers
- Find a way round
- Don't judge … just nudge!

# First conversations
## Exploring the issues

These two pages are designed to help you and your new Carbon Buddy to **ease yourselves into the project** you're about to undertake. They will enable you to stake out some of the territory, and become aware not only of the broad issues but also of what the pair of you have in common and where you are different.

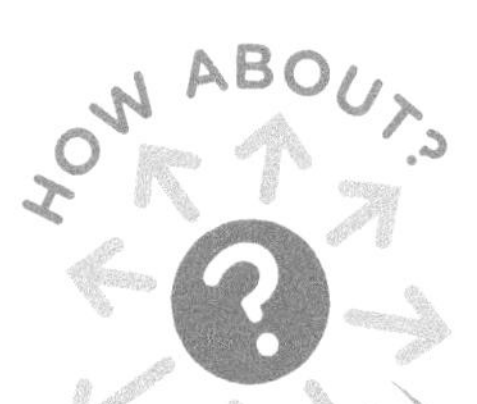


**Organising** a 'bauble' market before Christmas. Take your decorations and swap them for others. Everyone ends up with 'new' decorations!

**Don't try and do this quickly.** It needs time, and breaks in between conversations. It's to be savoured, reflected on, chewed over and perhaps amended after further consideration. It's about dipping your toes in the water. Time will allow both of you to begin to get a handle on where there might be scope for change, and where change might be more difficult. This relaxed preparation time together will pay dividends later.

**There are two groups of questions here:**

1 This page helps each of you explore your favourite activities and pastimes across aspects of your lifestyle. These aspects will crop up again and again throughout the manual.

2 The page opposite helps you explore your reactions to some relatively simple actions – most of them saving money – that you could take to kick-start your emissions reduction plans.

| Exploring the issues: your favourites | |
|---|---|
| **Food** What are your favourite foods ... and where do they come from? | **Recreation** What about leisure time? What are your favourite ways to relax? |
| **Personal transport** What are your main means of transport? What is your preferred method? | **Heating** How warm do you like to keep your house/flat? |
| **Events** What events have you been to in the last couple of years? Which were your favourites? | **Packaging** What do you like about packaging? Any particular favourites? |
| **Nature and the outdoors** What sort of contact and experience do you have of being close to nature and wild places? | **Medicines and personal care** What are the main products you use regularly? Which are essential? Which are your favourites? |
| **Household energy** What fuels do you use for heating, cooking, lighting, cleaning and home entertainment? | **Fashion and clothing** How often do you buy new clothes? And do you have favourite places to buy them? |
| **Holidays and travel** If you have taken any holidays in the last few years, which were your favourites? | **Hot water** Are you a shower or a bath person? How often do you bath, and how long do you stay in the shower? |

# Exploring the challenges

**Some quick wins:**

| Save **MONEY** by... | Heating your water at no more than 55°C | Substituting ONE holiday away with a holiday at home | Freezing, drying or bottling summer seasonal fruit and vegetables when they are cheap rather than buying them from abroad in the winter |
|---|---|---|---|
| Save **TIME** by... | Stopping doing some things, in order to free up an hour a week to work with your Carbon Buddy Manual | Reducing the time you spend shopping | Getting a circle of friends involved in the Carbon Buddy Project so that you can share the research |
| Save **ENERGY** by... | Turning down your heating thermostat to max 19°C, and wearing warmer clothes indoors | Getting thermal interliners for your curtains, and always closing them at night when it's cold | Ensuring all lights, and equipment on standby, are turned off when a room's left empty |
| Save **WASTE** by... | Downloading the water tap map at refill.org.uk (this could be replicated all over the world) | Starting small-scale composting if you're not already doing it | Politely returning all non-recyclable packaging to the shop where you bought it |

- For most people some of these will be really easy and some will be more difficult. Score them from 1 (very easy) to 10 (very difficult).

- Don't beat yourself up about those you find difficult.

- Instead, with the help of your Carbon Buddy try to figure out why the difficult ones seem to be so difficult. Don't worry if the answer doesn't seem to come quickly. It will probably emerge in time.

REFLECTION

**The thinking** What came out of our conversations exploring these issues?

Any surprises when discussing the challenges and quick wins?

# The action

Summarise any actions you have decided to take so far (pencil these into your short-term plan on pages 120–121).

CHAPTER

Switching to 100% green energy electricity tariff ... but beware 'greenwash'

INTRODUCTION

# What's a carbon footprint?

A footprint is what you leave behind in the sand. It's visible, and for the most part it's harmless. Your carbon footprint, on the other hand, is what you leave behind in the atmosphere. It's invisible and it's poisonous.

## Our personal pollution

We've seen news items about dangerous chemicals such as tanker spills on roads, chemical fires, and hazardous waste getting into rivers. If we're near enough to see them actually happening we fear them, we recoil, and we call urgently for professional help. But when poisonous chemicals are invisible, we live our lives as if they weren't there.

We call the visible ones pollution. We call the invisible ones carbon emissions or greenhouse gases.

But let's face it: they are pollution too. And many of them are our personal pollution.

Because our personal pollution is largely invisible to us, it's really hard to get a sense of how big it is overall, and which aspects of our lifestyles produce the most. The good news is that there is a way of measuring it, which makes it more tangible.

## Carbon calculators

There are measuring tools online: carbon footprint calculators. They're not perfect, but in most cases they're good enough to be a useful indicator. Like

# Making the invisible visible



medical x-rays, they are diagnostic tools which help us to take appropriate action. Trouble is, I've found that few people are aware of these tools, and even fewer have actually used them. In the next section I'll be asking you to have a crack at using one to:

measure your personal pollution and make it visible

## Primary and secondary footprints

But before we start, it's worth understanding the distinction between a primary carbon footprint and a secondary one. Our primary personal pollution comes from the fossil fuels we use for heating, cooling and transport, so we can influence our primary carbon footprint directly.

What is more difficult for us both to imagine and to influence is our secondary footprint, which arises from the things we buy: what raw materials are used, where they are sourced from, and how the products made from them are manufactured and distributed. Because we as consumers create the demand for these products and services, we are each responsible for a small part of these multiple supply chains and the pollution that emanates from them along the way. We can influence them indirectly by withdrawing our custom, by stopping buying items that we believe to have unacceptable carbon footprints or food miles, and by putting pressure on the suppliers.

# What's a supply chain?

## ... and who's in the driving seat?

### How the fossil fuel economy works

#### ENERGY

Energy, energy, and yet more energy. The fossil fuel economy is a voracious consumer of energy. You might even say it's addicted to energy. And because it's the fossil fuel economy that has provided us with so many benefits over the last century or more, we have become caught up in that addiction too. We are, after all, not referred to as 'consumers' accidentally. We are consumers of all that energy embedded in the products and services we spend or money on. **We are the appetite.**

#### RAW MATERIALS

The fossil fuel economy is also built on the idea of raw materials. That means two things:

- **Digging stuff** out of the ground (coal, oil, gas and ore) which gets converted into raw materials. This uses energy and results in environmental degradation.

- **Growing stuff** which gets converted into raw materials. More energy. More pesticide pollution. More soil depletion. Less biodiversity.

#### THE SUPPLY CHAIN

All these raw materials are built into components (more energy) which in turn are transported to various locations around the world (more energy) to be assembled into part-finished or fully finished products (more energy). They then get sent to distributors (more energy), who in turn deliver them to retailers (more energy), who often deliver them to us, the end consumer (more energy). There it is: the invisible supply chain revealed.

**At every step (and for some products there are literally thousands of steps), fossil fuel energy is consumed.** And that means that at every step there are more noxious greenhouse gases being released. All to satisfy our appetites.

### The fossil fuel economy: booster drugs

The fossil fuel economy has evolved some clever but largely invisible drugs to feed its addiction. The first of these is **planned obsolescence** – deliberately making things that don't last long, so that we, the consumers, replace them or upgrade them before it's really necessary. More stuff. More energy. More waste.

The second drug is **the idea of what's fashionable or what's popular.** I guess as consumers we'd like to believe that these ideas are a reflection of what we like. But it's not quite like that. Advertising and the media have a crucial role in telling us what we like, in stoking up our wants, and defining for us what is 'desirable'. More stuff. More energy. More waste.

The third drug is **experiential marketing;** as we find we have more and more of what we want, we run out of products to buy. So we start to buy experiences instead. Less stuff. But still lots of energy. And waste.

## The fossil fuel economy: the psychology

Advertising creates needs out of our wants. Real needs are things we really *can't* do without: food, water, shelter, and respect and love. But products which are fashionable or luxurious or desirable are presented as things we can't do without ... that new dress, that new iPhone, that yummy cake. **We end up feeling that we can't possibly do without these things.** We have, without realising it, become addicted. When people imagine not having these 'needs' met, they talk about 'sacrifice' and 'loss' (for more on this, see pages 71–72).

There's another fundamental psychological factor operating: the need to feel we belong, that others approve of us. When overdone, this becomes group pressure, the pressure to conform. This is a very strong driver of buying decisions. Kids plead with parents for some new gadget: 'everyone at school's got one!' Social media vilifies those who don't conform as 'saddos'. Fear of being left out. Brand loyalty. Keeping up with the Joneses. The pressures are sometimes subtle, sometimes blatant, always there.

But just imagine if these same psychological drivers could be steered towards products and services that were helping to grow the green economy. What if they became the desirable, the fashionable, the favoured brands? A few individuals shifting their buying patterns get labelled as barmy. A few more, and then more and more take them up – and **suddenly you have a tipping point when the purchases become mainstream** and it seems that everyone wants them. The good news here is that the people involved are not only expressing the new wants, but also expressing the deepest and oldest of our true needs ... the need to help ensure the survival of our species.

## The big shift: putting the consumer in the driving seat

The increasing rate of collateral damage from the current system demands our attention. We don't need to see ourselves as victims of the economic system. Instead, we can decide that old consumerism is out, and that we have the right to assert ourselves and become the drivers of the new consumerism. I can see several shifts and fault lines developing in the workings of the fossil fuel economy. These are not, strictly speaking, shifts in the system. **They are much more shifts in ourselves which are beginning to be reflected in the system.** We're beginning to value different things. They are the new products and services which we're now demanding– and the behaviour change and the new attitudes and mindsets will redefine many of the drivers of the economy.

One example of such a shift is that many in the younger generation are **challenging the very idea of fashion, fashion trends and being fashionable.** They are asking why we need fashion at all. They are rejecting being slaves to fashion in favour of clothes being an expression of individuality rather than conformity.

It is such shifts that I will explore later, in steps 17–19, which **look at the new 'cool consumerism'** (or how to use our money to make a difference.)

# Measuring your carbon footprint

STEP

## Collecting information

Pretty much EVERYTHING we do and buy has some form of pollution associated with it. Trouble is we can't SEE most of that. But we can make it 'visible' by MEASURING it. We can now use the power of the internet to make that measurement process way simpler than it has ever been.

So let me introduce you to my favourite online carbon footprint calculator. It's called Giki Zero ... and here is the link:

zero.giki.earth

These guys have found a way to break down a complicated process into bite-size chunks (you know about me and bite-size chunks!). This makes it much more manageable and, dare I say it, even quite fun. But here's a bit of a health warning:

Do it step by step. First thing is to gather as much information as you can about your consumption of different products and services. The master list is opposite. The lines in purple, and their related units of measurement, are the ones used by Giki Zero. I've added a few more elements in green that may be relevant to you. You can calculate these using a different carbon footprint calculator:

**carbonfootprint.com/calculator.aspx**

### A few words about units of measurement

Giki Zero uses UK£ for money and mostly metric for other measures. I've summarised their units in the table opposite. If your local currency is different, or if your country uses different measures, then a quick conversion using Google will translate your local measures into those used by Giki Zero.

### Turning these units into measures of your carbon footprint

Now here's the clever bit. Click on the FOOTPRINTS tab at the top of the Giki Zero home page. Pop your figures into the relevant section and up comes the KILOGRAMS OF $CO_2$ emitted by that item! Make a note of that figure and write it down in the summary chart on the following two pages. Here's your overview. You're ready for the next step.

| Lifestyle Elements | Units |
|---|---|
| **Home** | |
| Oil | Litres |
| Waste | Bags per week |
| Water | Litres |
| Electricity | Kilowatt Hours (kwh) |
| Gas | Cubic metres or kwh |
| Maintenance | Pre-calculated average |
| Coal | Metric tonnes |
| LPG | Litres |
| Propane | Litres |
| Wood | Metric tonnes |
| **Food** | |
| Food waste | 5 of your food |
| Diet | Portions |
| Pet food | By breed |
| **Transport** | |
| Bus/coach | Journeys |
| Tube/subway | Journeys |
| Motorbike | Annual mileage |
| Rail (local and international) | Journey time |
| Ship/ferry | Estimated length |
| Taxi | Journeys |
| Car | Miles or kilometres pa |
| Flights | Departure/arrival destination |
| Tram | Miles or km |
| **Purchases** | |
| Clothing | Itemised or estimates category |
| Electricals | Itemised (with prompts) |
| Personal care | Prompts |
| Appliances | Prompts |
| Furniture | Estimates or itemised |
| Cleaning | Estimates |
| Books/papers/magazines | £ pa |
| Vehicle purchase (divide by likely years of ownership) | £ |
| **Services** | |
| Accomodation/hotels | Nights away/prompts |
| Financial services and investments | £ value savings/investments |
| Pharmacy/medical | Pre-calculated average |
| Recreation | Pre-calculated average |
| Paid-for education | £ |

# STEP 4 Summarising the numbers

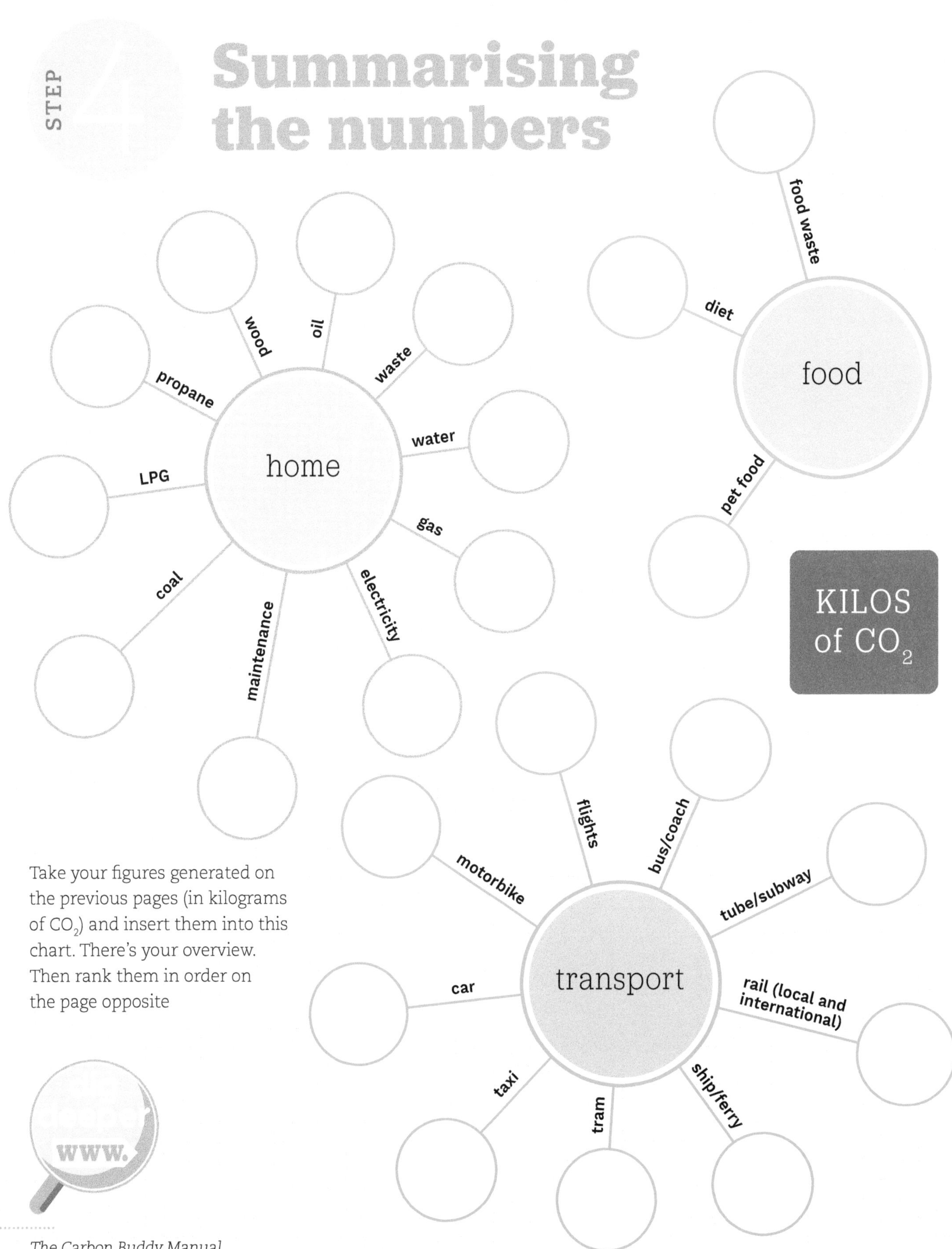


Take your figures generated on the previous pages (in kilograms of $CO_2$) and insert them into this chart. There's your overview. Then rank them in order on the page opposite

Rank the categories below in order of most polluting to least polluting.

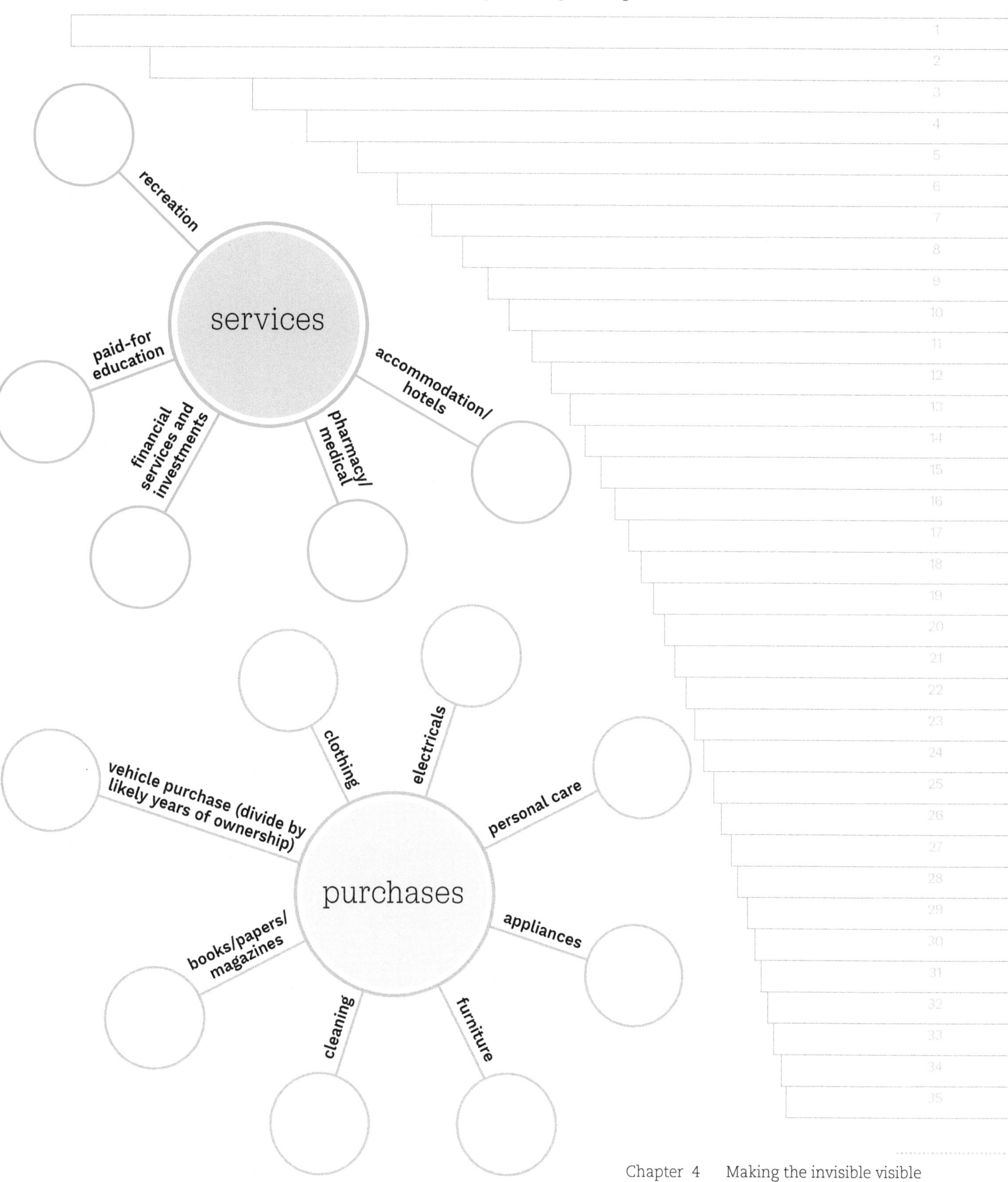

STEP

# Picturing your personal pollution

Continuing the theme of trying to visualise this invisible personal pollution, here's an opportunity to get creative. Here's a blank canvas for you to create your own artistic representation of all the sources of personal pollution that support your current lifestyle. If you want some prompts to stimulate your thinking, take a look at **carbonbuddyproject.org.** Let your imagination run riot!

# Connecting with others
## The dress rehearsal

### Talk to people!

At the climate change conference I mentioned earlier, one of the speakers told us to **'just starting talking to people about it'.** (I love that word 'just': just re-program the central heating timer, just slash your carbon footprint, just fly to the moon. It's hardly ever quite as simple as the word implies.)

It felt a bit strange initially. We started tentatively and cautiously, being careful not to seem evangelical or pushy. But gradually, with a little practice, we began to find the right words, the right tone of voice and the right body language. **Our confidence grew,** and we started to understand more about how others saw the problem.

### Conversation starters

Here are a few ways of starting a conversation that we have found work quite well:

- Find opportunities for casual conversation at the bus stop, the school playground, the pub, the club, the class, the mosque, and at local events.
- In a supermarket queue, chip in with remarks like 'I've just looked at where this fruit comes from, and do you know it comes all the way from South America?'
- Or 'All this plastic packaging drives me nuts!'
- Adapt the 'favourites' questions in Step 2 on page 32.
- Casually mention that you've just been calculating your carbon footprint and how you feel about it.
- Slip in the **odd bit of climate change speak** – food miles, renewable energy, electric bikes, rain forests, carbon footprint, ecopreneur – and see if you get a reaction.
- Do look on the website (in the Information Gateway) for a brilliant guide to having climate conversations. It's full of insight and practical tips.

### No-go areas

**But do tread carefully and sensitively, particularly at this early stage.**

- Don't mention climate change or the climate crisis or global heating. It's too huge. Talk about specific things that can be done.
- Don't ask people what they think. It puts them on the spot. Talk instead about what **you** are doing.
- Don't push it. **Make the interactions brief, casual, polite and short.** If it leads to a longer conversation, that's great.

I think you'll find it's actually quite fun and you certainly learn a lot by people's reactions (or lack of them). And you begin to feel good because you're now starting to **do something**! And you never know, you just *might* sow your first pollution reduction seeds which blow on the wind and grow elsewhere.

REFLECTION

# The thinking

## A pause for reflection

We've already covered a lot of ground since we started our ride together. I don't know about you, but I like to pause from time to time on a journey. The timing of this break is quite good: a refuelling stop before you go on to bring together what you have done to date and turn it into your first personal pollution reduction plan.

On the other hand, if you're one of those people who likes to press on, then you will anyway, won't you!

Here are a few suggested reflective questions to ponder with your Carbon Buddy:

- How are we doing so far?
- Any particular messages we want to hang onto?
- Any bits that we haven't really understood that might be worth revisiting? (No shame in that.)
- How was it talking to other people about what we were doing?
- One highlight each.
- One lowlight each … and how to avoid repeating it.
- Onwards and upwards: any resolutions for the next stage?

# The action

Summarise any actions here and pencil them into your final plan (see pages 120–125).

CHAPTER 5

HOW ABOUT?

Imagining how you could give a new lease of life to a second-hand product with a little bit of creativity and craft

INTRODUCTION

# Managing time and energy

## A sense of calm urgency

Make no mistake. This is big and complex. You will already have a sense of the range of actions you might want to take. You may already have a gut feel for how much energy and time they will take. The most common way in which people fail is by **trying to take on too much and getting frazzled and overwhelmed.** That's the road to burnout. No point in going down that route.

What you're after is to be able to proceed with a sense of calm urgency and persistence (where did we hear that before?) You'll find that less is more, because the more you succeed in doing, the more you feel energised to do more. It's a virtuous circle.

## Three practical principles

I have found these three very simple principles really useful as I come to plan out what I want to do. They apply in all sorts of other situations too.

### 1. Bite-size chunks:

- The basic idea here is that if you have something big to do, break it down into smaller elements or stages. Start with your end objective, and then work backwards, summarising all the things that need doing to get there.
- You might find it useful to write those elements down on cards or sticky notes and lay them out on a large sheet of paper so you can rearrange them easily to work out the order in which they need to be done.

# Feeling in control



You can also estimate how long each element will take, and build up your overall time scale bottom upwards.

## 2. The perfect is the enemy of the good enough:

And above all don't let the pursuit of some kind of mythical 'perfect answer' (frequently demanded of you by others, and sometimes by yourself) paralyse you into inaction. In these exceptional circumstances, good enough is good enough.

## 3. Think 5 years/ 260 weeks:

Try to set realistic expectations from the beginning. You can always get more ambitious as you go along – but failing and therefore scaling back your plans is discouraging.

But do put in lots of milestones along the route. Getting to each one gives a sense of achievement … and provides an excuse for a celebration.

It's a long ride; not a sprint. Tortoise rather than hare. Keeping up a gentle, steady momentum is everything.

# Prioritisation: Where do I start?

You can't do everything at once. Here is where we start to get a feel for what can be done sooner and what will need to be done later. But this is early days, your first action planning session. Remember: don't try and get it perfect.

**Remember this from page 19?**

MY PERSONAL COOL PLANET GOAL

**How to make the biggest impact I can in the shortest possible time?**

This gives us two simple principles to guide us on where to start:

1 Where can I make the BIGGEST reduction in my personal pollution?

2 Where can I make the QUICKEST reduction in my personal pollution?

# Summarise the big ones ... and list the small ones

This is where you bring together the many thoughts and discussions you have had so far and put them into something resembling a plan! This is where you begin to commit, to go from intention to action.

I suggest making two lists below. The first brings your top ten sources of personal pollution from your summary on pages 42 and 43, and the second pulls together other actions stemming from your first conversations about the issues and challenges (pages 31 and 32) or anything else you have decided you want to do.

| **The BIG ones** Biggest polluter at the top | | **The SMALL ones** Biggest potential impact at the top (rough estimate) | |
|---|---|---|---|
| | | | |
| | | | |
| | | | |
| | | | |
| | | | |

# Mapping priorities

The graph below gives you a simple visual way of putting your lists from Step 8 into some sort of order. On the **vertical axis you are representing the relative SIZE of the impacts** you can make and **on the horizontal axis you are representing the SPEED or time scales** over which you can make those impacts. I suggest you do this mapping using pencil initially.

Notice that my 'measures' of size and speed are deliberately crude. With the size axis you do have some numbers you can use (from your emissions calculation), **but for me the main point is the relative impacts.** For the speed axis, I have merely put short-term, medium-term and long-term. **You will define these to suit your circumstances.** But, because of the urgency of making pollution reductions overall, I'd like to suggest that long-term does not stretch beyond five years!

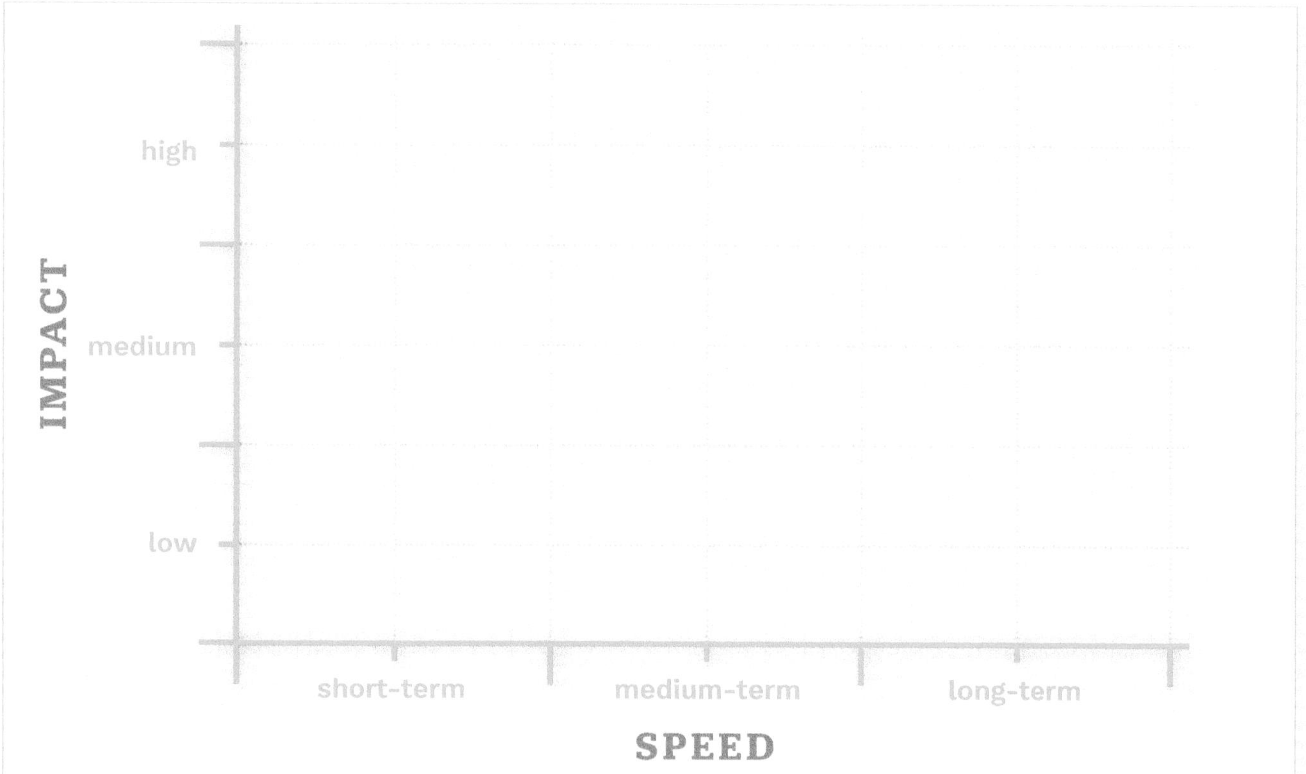


Having done this first draft action summary, transfer it to the main planning pages (pages 120–125) where you can set it out with more space. Again, I suggest you do it in pencil at this stage.

CHAPTER 6

HOW ABOUT?

Finding practical and skilled retired people who could provide a repair café service in your local community

INTRODUCTION

# Sowing new seeds

## The exponential challenge

In Step 6 I invited you to step out and start talking to people in a very low-key way about carbon footprints and the like. Besides getting used to having these types of conversations, you will, I'm hoping, be getting a sense of the scale of the third major challenge that we face:

> How to trigger an exponential rise in the number of individuals and organisations taking action both 'here' and 'there'.

The question is how can we as lone individuals find ways to draw in large numbers of other people? In this section you will see that I have a cunning plan! It's called propagation.

## The growing cycle

I like growing vegetables. I especially like the moment when I sow the seed in some compost and put it in the propagator, the nice warm cosy environment which encourages the seed to sprout and become a seedling. I like the moment, too, when I take that young seedling and plant it out in the garden to grow on. It needs attention for a while. It needs watering, maybe staking, but quite soon it becomes established. It's strong enough to draw the nutrients from its new soil and grow by itself. I have completed my task as a propagator. The plant will eventually produce its own seeds **and so the cycle can begin again,** sometimes spontaneously and sometimes with further human intervention.

# Propagation

# Time to think bigger



## The role of the Carbon Buddy propagator

Now I'm asking you to consider becoming a propagator too. Think of giving seeds to new Carbon Buddies and nurturing their early growth until each seed has grown sufficiently to become established. Some will need more nurturing, some less. And some won't thrive at all. That's how it is.

Although taking steps to draw others in might seem to be a bit of a drag (more so for introverts than extroverts, I suspect), it also has a very important positive function. Whilst it's relatively easy to get going with enthusiasm, over time it's more difficult to keep going. Rather as the marathon runners use pacemakers and take slugs of energy drinks along the way, **new people joining us on the ride inject new energy and new ideas.** They in turn become the catalysts to draw in other people and so the process unfolds, gathering momentum apace with the help of the internet, growing exponentially and going viral within countries, and – given many people's **international friendships and links – between countries.** That's what we need to happen. Let's take the first steps in this propagation process right now.

# Reaching outwards

## Here's a personal network map

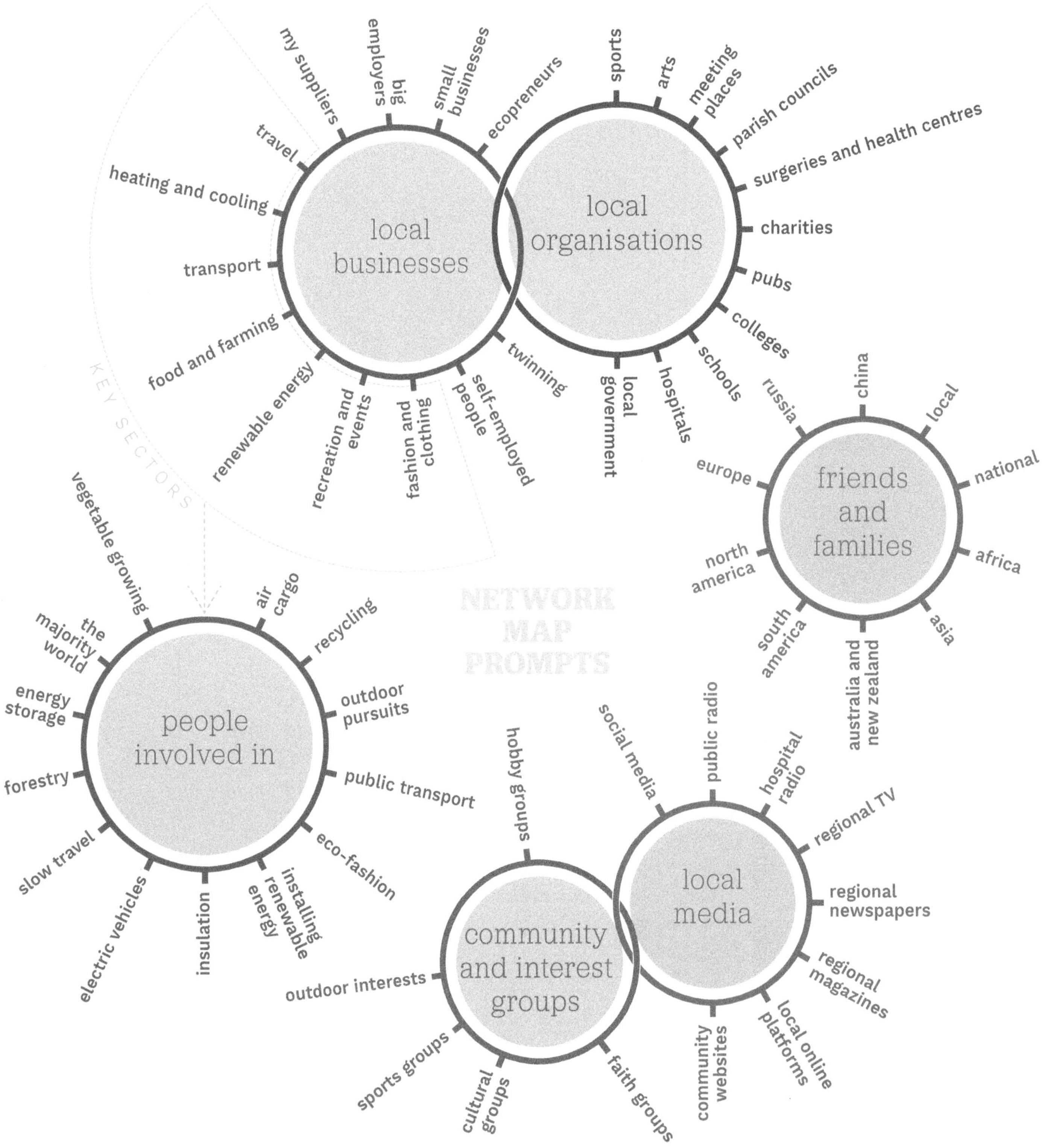

NETWORK MAP PROMPTS

KEY SECTORS

**local businesses**

- my suppliers
- big employers
- small businesses
- ecopreneurs
- twinning
- self-employed people
- fashion and clothing
- recreation and events
- renewable energy
- food and farming
- transport
- heating and cooling
- travel

**local organisations**

- sports
- arts
- meeting places
- parish councils
- surgeries and health centres
- charities
- pubs
- colleges
- schools
- hospitals
- local government

**friends and families**

- china
- local
- national
- africa
- asia
- australia and new zealand
- south america
- north america
- europe
- russia

**people involved in**

- air cargo
- recycling
- outdoor pursuits
- public transport
- eco-fashion
- installing renewable energy
- insulation
- electric vehicles
- slow travel
- forestry
- energy storage
- the majority world
- vegetable growing

**local media**

- public radio
- hospital radio
- regional TV
- regional newspapers
- regional magazines
- local online platforms
- community websites
- social media

**community and interest groups**

- hobby groups
- faith groups
- cultural groups
- sports groups
- outdoor interests

## Your personal network map

Use this space to start mapping your network of personal relationships and contacts.
An example of a network map is shown opposite, to help you get going.

# Attracting new Buddies

## Purposeful conversations

### It's that exponential challenge again!

On page 46 you took the first steps in talking to strangers. At the end of that page I used the image of you sowing pollution reduction seeds which might then grow somewhere else. Hopefully by now you have begun to take some actual steps towards reducing your own personal pollution and are beginning to feel more confident in talking about your carbon reduction experiences.

The next stage of the ride is rather different. In addition to concentrating on implementing your own carbon reduction plan, I'm asking you to play a part in getting lots of other people involved. To be effective, we need to get literally **millions of people worldwide working on reducing their personal pollution.** That's a big ask. I'm sure your experience so far will make you feel confident in approaching new people more purposefully to help expand the Carbon Buddy Project. Here's how you can help make this happen:

### Map your network

**I bet you know many more people than you think!** Take a look at the Network Map on page 54 and use it as a prompt to start listing people and organisations that you might want to approach. Your Carbon Buddy will be doing the same.

### Start looking for new carbon buddies

Look at your two maps and use them to discuss who you think you might want to invite to join you as you grow from a Buddy Pair into a Carbon Buddy Group. Think about how you're going to approach people and what sort of approach will be the most likely to make them open to the possibility of getting involved.

### Propagate: finding new fertile ground

A work organisation is a great place to get a whole new group of people involved. Colleagues can either agree to work together on their own personal pollution, or they may suggest setting up one or more groups to look at the pollution of the whole organisation and come up with a plan. Equally Carbon Buddy groups can take root in schools, community groups, faith groups, extended families ... the possibilities are endless. **If you can see some fertile ground, go for it.** Result. You've become a Carbon Buddy Propagator!

HOW ABOUT?

**Asking** restaurants where their ingredients are sourced from

## Getting your new group off the ground

- I suggest you identify a maximum of two more people at this stage; **groups larger than four tend to become unwieldy.** If you find more than two people, you can always approach them to encourage them to set up their own pair or group.

- It's good to bring in **new ideas and new energy.** Perhaps deliberately ask people who are a bit different from you?

- **Friends in other countries** might be particularly interesting, to get a different perspective. They will also help to spread the idea internationally. You could run a group with people joining by Skype, Facetime or Google Hangouts.

- Invite them to join you. Decide how often you are going to talk together and where (eg in someone's house, online, at the pub, in the park).

- Make sure you make them feel welcome and explain what you've done so far. It's difficult coming into an existing working group, so be sensitive to that. Remember what it was like for you when you were just starting off.

You now have a Carbon Buddy Group!

## Information Gateway

I've mentioned this already but it's worth repeating. Hop over to the Information Gateway section of the Carbon Buddy Project website and on page 56 you'll see a link to a seriously useful guide to having constructive and fruitful climate change conversations. Highly recommended.

# A few tips to make your Carbon Buddy group effective

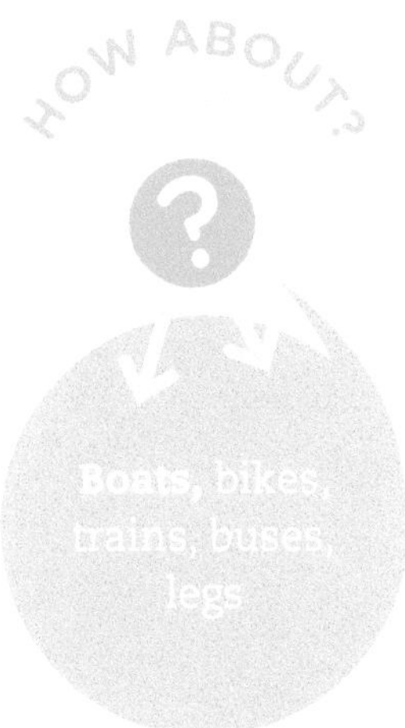


Meetings, whether the people are in the same room or online together, can be shambolic. Poorly run meetings leave everyone feeling frustrated, and what they produce is few results and widespread dissatisfaction.

Here are a few very simple disciplines to ensure that your Carbon Buddy meetings are both productive and enjoyable. Share the responsibility for ensuring that the conversation stays on track.

THE GRUMP DUMP Max ten minutes, for everyone to offload all their climate change frustrations and distractions, rail against the politicians and all those they don't see eye to eye with, to moan about all those who just don't get it. Feeling better? Now to work.

REPORT BACK BRIEFLY ON WHAT EACH OF YOU HAVE DONE SINCE YOU LAST TALKED Max ten minutes. Celebrate successes, and try to understand failures. But don't beat yourself up (or any other group members) about failures. Don't wallow. Move on.

HOW ABOUT?
?
**Buying** better quality clothes and enjoying wearing them for much longer


ACTION PHASE Each person has a 15-minute slot. This is their time. Don't hog it with your stuff. The job of the rest of the group is to help each fellow Carbon Buddy to:

- **Identify** where they want to focus their energy.
- **Be clear** about what steps they need to take to start making progress.
- **Be realistic.** No point in getting stressed and discouraged by biting off more than they can chew.
- **Commit** to action. It's a kind of pledge that they make to the others.

Every few meetings, find a topic that feels a bit outside someone's comfort zone. Explore it together without judgement.

THEN THE SOCIAL BIT! The first three agenda items are purposeful but fun work. End with relaxing fun, however you do that. Celebrate your progress.

REFLECTION

## The thinking

- When I was doing my network map, how did it feel?
- What struck me about it?
- What was the most difficult thing about attracting new Carbon Buddies?
- Any success in spreading it to other countries?
- If not, does my network map suggest any other routes I could use?

## The action

Summarise any actions here and pencil them into your final plan as well (see pages 120–125).

CHAPTER 7

> "We need to mourn what is lost, value what remains. And not just the natural world; we need to mourn the end of the fossil fuels age, which, for all its dirt and danger, was also exceptionally affluent, mobile, and exciting. The low-carbon world will have new pleasures, but no longer the sweet roar of the Ford Mustang V8."
>
> GEORGE MARSHALL

INTRODUCTION

# Reflections on change

In this section we take a well-earned break on our ride. It's time for a change of pace, a different viewpoint, time to reflect. We talk about climate change. **But to change the climate we are going to have to change ourselves.** And that's not always as simple as it may seem because it's asking us to change some of our behaviours, our values, our habits, and our ways of solving problems. And many of those are deeply ingrained.

## The psychology of behaviour change

The psychology of behaviour change is a well-established academic topic. Trouble is that a lot of what is written is impenetrable to most of the population! Much of my professional life was spent trying to sift out the valuable and useful ideas in the field and to translate them into more understandable language. So here goes. I'm arrogant enough (or stupid enough) to believe that I can give you **all you need to know about the psychology of change in just 14 short pages!** My cunning plan is to introduce you to the psychology of change without your even realising it!

## Helping and hindering forces

The section is divided broadly into two parts. The first five topics talk about psychological processes that seem to help us to change. The second six topics talk about factors that hinder the process of change. The simple secret is to focus on **reducing or overcoming the hindering forces** whilst quietly building the helping forces.

# Interlude



## Making the invisible visible ... again

Much of what I'm talking about here lies within ourselves. To many it is invisible. Although invisible, it has profound effects and consequences which I hope I can throw some light on. Another problem is that, because it isn't exactly everyday conversation, **many people don't really have a vocabulary to talk about it.** And what you can't talk about you can't understand. And what you can't understand you can't begin to think about changing. I see this section as being about providing a basic change management toolkit.

I suggest, as you go through, that at each stage you reflect with your Carbon Buddy on how each topic relates to each of you and your own behaviour. If you can get a better handle on your own reactions to change, not only will that help you to change, but also begin to help you to help 'them' to change. So, sit back in the saddle, and enjoy this different view.

HOW ABOUT?

**Finding** someone with a thermal imaging camera or night time binoculars to see where the heat loss from your house comes out

# Helping factors ...

## People power:
## how to be a quiet change-maker

Rosabeth Moss Kanter was a professor of organisation management at Yale University way back in the last century. She wrote a brilliant book called *The Change Masters*. She found that people who were successful innovators went about things in a particular way which distinguished them from those who preserved the status quo.

The change makers' key skill was their ability to cultivate and mobilise networks of people to help them bring about innovation and change. They did not, and could not, act effectively alone. She challenged the common idea that this type of influencing and networking was somehow 'political' or self-serving. What she found was that these individuals were not acting in a narrow self-interested way, but were searching for a wider objective that was important in some way, and around which people could coalesce. This type of networking enabled them to pull together the many resources, such as the money, materials, information, knowhow, time and people, required to realise the objective.

This ability and style of making things happen she called 'positive power', driven by a collective focus and shared sense of a wider importance and urgency. In contrast, she defined 'negative power' as the power to stop things happening, usually driven by a narrower sense of self-interest, or anxiety about change.

### Different 'currencies'

Money is but one resource that some can bring. But all of us have within us these less tangible resources which are even more valuable to this challenge, and which need to be released:

- our time, our passion, our knowledge, our networks, our persuasiveness, our experience, our confidence, our bravery, our determination, our persistence.

The whole thrust of this book is about how to harness and focus this infinite pool of energy and talent across the globe.

# The power of purpose: discovering your resolve

## What's *really* important here?

Why are we doing this? It's all about things that are dear to us:

- It's about leaving behind us a viable and satisfying future for our immediate families.
- It's about leaving the natural world in a state where it can support the lives of future generations.
- It's about creating lifestyles that cause zero collateral damage to people and to the planet.
- It's about wanting to be part of something big, something positive and transformational.

And in achieving this it's all about:

- Redefining extravagance ... spending with a purpose.
- Redefining parsimony ... saving with a purpose.
- Redefining many of our rights and substituting them with responsibilities.
- Redefining luxury and pampering into caring for the other (the future, nature, the earth's eco-systems).

# The power of persistence

## discovering inner strength

### Discovering your determination

We have all seen and heard stories of ordinary people who suddenly find themselves in extraordinary situations. Some crumble, but many, many others discover hidden inner strengths they never knew that they possessed. This is usually triggered when external events produce a situation they care deeply about and which they feel is both important and urgent. I find myself thinking particularly of parents whose children are suddenly struck by disaster or serious illness, or people who have been subject to a great injustice, but there are many other examples.

What these people discover is a deep and dogged persistence which keeps them going despite all the barriers they face. And the more barriers they surmount, the stronger and more confident they become. They simply will not give up.

In some way we all share a parental responsibility for our planet. And now that she is in such deep trouble, hopefully we will discover that inner sense of determination and persistence which will be needed to keep going.

# Nudging
# the influence of others

## Setting an example: a true story

A guy who lived in a village wanted an electric car. There were none in the area. He told his mates in the pub and met with ridicule. 'It won't work,' they said. 'Not enough range. No charging points.' He went ahead anyhow. The first day his next-door neighbour came round to have a snoop, and the next day he gave a friend a lift to the pub. Both grudgingly said they could see the attraction. Time passed. Within three months, there were eight electric cars within five miles of the village! 'Electric cars grow in clusters,' said the salesman who told me this story.

# Drawing inspiration from others

those we admire

## Greta

A young Swedish schoolgirl called Greta Thunberg caught the world's imagination.

She confronted us adults with her fear that the scale of the climate change threat is escalating exponentially whilst our response to it is at best inadequate and at worst deliberately irresponsible.

*Some of the placards at the strikes she inspired:*

- There is no Planet B
- I'll do my homework if you do yours
- If you can't be adults, we can
- Stop talking: DO something

# Hindering factors ...

## Time to stop picking holes: no more 'yes buts'

In a situation like this it's only human nature to focus on the negatives – what we lose, what we dislike, what's wrong with a particular course of action, why others are a bigger problem than we are. These reactions not only sap everyone's energy but are seen by their proponents as a justification for inaction.

My response to them is this. Climate science (just like medicine and many other aspects of science) is not a precise science. It cannot predict absolutely precisely. You can always find holes to pick, if that's your game. But picking holes, whilst being good sport to try and derail your opponent, also diverts and distracts us from discussing the serious problems that are creeping up on us, and even more so on our children and grandchildren.

There comes a time when on the balance of probability (the test widely used in evaluating evidence in a court of law), the feared events become more and more likely to happen within a shorter and shorter time frame, and picking holes purely to justify inaction becomes unacceptable. On the balance of probability, and as a precaution to try to prevent the anticipated highly damaging events, the timescales for action and the scale of action have to be accelerated markedly. This is no longer alarmist. It is realist. Those intent purely on playing the game of picking holes will have to be left behind. The rest of us will just get on and do stuff.

# Defusing negative energy

## avoiding diversions and distractions

### Beware: it's a trap! Don't fall into it.

**Clever clogs:** some people aren't able to listen and instead may blast you with a facts dump, usually unrelated to what you're talking about.

**Response:** Try asking: 'I'm not sure why you're telling me that. I'm talking about … I'd be interested to hear your ideas about that.'

**I'm perfect, you're stupid:** the implication is that you've failed to consider all manner of things. It's a kind of disguised ridicule.

**Response:** Two can play at that game: 'The perfect is the enemy of the good enough. Urgency demands acting without knowing everything. Tell me at what point you think we will know enough to be able to act?'

**Response:** 'On the contrary. **Do it** unless there is a compelling reason not to do it. The perfect never arrives.'

**It's them that's the problem:** no point in doing anything until all those foreigners stop gas guzzling/burning coal/wasting food etc.

**Response:** Try saying something like: 'Those are indeed big problems. But they are no excuse for my inaction – I'm only concerned with what we as individuals can do. But as this is of concern to you, why don't you look into which pressure groups are campaigning internationally on those issues and give them your active support?'

### A useful generic response

'Let me send you the details of the relevant section of a highly respected book on this topic. I'd be interested to know what you make of it' (Ref the books on pages 116–117).

**Do it** unless there is a **truly** compelling reason not to. **The perfect never arrives.**

# Less selling and more listening

## The magic of empathy

The reality is that you're selling an idea which many people will find uncomfortable. It's so easy to go on selling harder, keep pushing harder. But that tends to trigger stronger resistance. Result, impasse. Better to get to understand their discomfort and find ways to reduce those resisting forces. Often, when you really listen genuinely to detractors, tune into them, respect them, and don't make them feel bad, you can suggest ways or provide information which will allay their concerns or discomfort, and their resistance melts away.

**Let's reframe this as:**

- How to get a better understanding of this person's negative reaction.
- How to understand where they're coming from.

**Here are a few suggestions for active listening:**

- 'I can see you feel strongly about that. Tell me more about your concerns.'
- 'Help me to understand more about how you came to that conclusion.'
- 'What lies behind your question?'
- 'I'm sorry … it wasn't my intention to make you feel angry/guilty/etc. Help me understand what it was that I said that made you feel that way.'

**Be prepared to:**

- explore their agenda rather than yours,
- agree with them, and acknowledge that they may have a point,
- disclose and talk about your own dilemmas, feelings, doubts and ambivalences, too.

Have a phrase ready which goes something like 'You're right – there are many problems with doing this stuff … but I've come to the conclusion that I can't use that as an excuse to do nothing. If we waited for everything to be perfectly clear, sorted before taking any action, nothing would change. Something has to change.'

Whatever you do, don't get drawn into an argument.

Don't get heated … stay cool!

# Habits:
## die hard

We have all developed habits, perhaps even more so as we get older. Habitual behaviour is a bit like running on autopilot. You don't really have to engage your thinking brain because the habitual behaviour just seems to happen. Many aspects of our fossil-fuelled lifestyles are akin to habits. There is much we take for granted, and much we do on autopilot without realising that we always have a choice.

Habits do have a positive function, in that they mean we don't have to decide every moment of every day what we're going to do or how we're going to behave. Without them we would be quivering wrecks of indecision. Which is perhaps why having to change our habits is so profoundly unsettling.

Most of us, even the most cynical, don't want to feel that our lifestyle habits are damaging others. In this instance, then, maybe try thinking of the planet as a living person. But think, too, of members of your family two generations hence. Few would want to wilfully damage their life support systems irreparably. We do have choices.

How, then, to change our habits? Well, the first step is to be challenged to become aware of them and to become aware of their negative consequences, especially the invisible damage they cause. Being with a Carbon Buddy in a supportive environment is just the place to deliver and explore those challenges without retreating into the defensive.

Then start thinking and talking about how you might replace that with a more positive habit that has beneficial consequences. Really focus on the positives both for you and for others.

Then look at the problems of changing, and try, with your Carbon Buddy, to navigate the transition. There will be a sense of loss relating to what you're leaving behind. There will be ups and downs as you try to establish new lifestyle patterns. Because habits are sometimes deeply ingrained, they don't change easily or quickly. But if you keep at it, over time the new habit will become established, releasing new energy. At that point it becomes part of the routine, the new autopilot, and you'll wonder how it was that you ever did anything different!

# Brick walls or protective shells?

## On curiosity, creativity & respect

LESSON NO 1: Curiosity didn't kill the cat! It helps us find a way out of tricky situations. Some people you meet will be fixed on 'transmit' whilst others more readily 'receive'. It's easier talking to people who receive. You listen to them, they listen to you, you bounce ideas and feelings to and fro. The conversation begins to explore all the interesting, challenging, and even threatening issues this book is about.

But what of the ones who are fixed on transmit? Perhaps be curious and ask yourself (or them) why?

LESSON NO 2: There's no point bashing your head against a brick wall. Psychological brick walls are often the way we protect ourselves, from threats real or imagined.

How to get a message over the wall? Many people can't imagine how to change their lives without making very unpalatable sacrifices. They see only minuses. Can you imagine, and so help them imagine, the pluses, both short-term and long-term? Are there other ways of feeling good which are less dependent on all the stuff that consumes carbon?

Here's a real-life snippet: my wife started a conversation with a well-off friend of ours about sports cars. He said, 'But I just *love* the sound the engine makes when I start up that car.' He's the most loving family man you could ever hope to meet, so she said 'I know you love your children and grandchildren more, and care about their future more'. End of conversation. Message received? He's beginning to ask questions about the climate crisis that he didn't ask before.

LESSON NO 3: There's no point trying to make people feel bad or guilty for not doing enough. It's about helping them feel good about doing something, and then a bit more.

LESSON NO 4: If you can get people interested and curious about climate change by demonstrating curiosity yourself, you've already done a lot. Most people's brick walls are not as thick as you might think. If we can help other people think about climate change as a series of practical problems which are solvable, we can help reduce the fear that keeps us all behind those walls. People hate feeling helpless. But with a nudge from a friend, and a bit of creativity, what once seemed impossible suddenly seems to be within our grasp.

# Loss and sacrifice for the greater good?

## Accepting a new reality

'I think one of the most difficult aspects of climate change is its emotional significance. Giving up a way of life that's been our privilege to enjoy in recent years requires a major emotional readjustment.

'Our generation (the baby boomers) have enjoyed pleasures which previous generations couldn't begin to dream of. And future generations may well be denied them because of our own actions. Most of us have come to take for granted our freedom to travel easily and at speed, to enjoy a wide variety of foods from all over the world, to pad around our warm homes in a tee-shirt and bare feet even in winter, to buy fashionable clothes and get rid of them when they no longer please us. How do we feel about no longer having these pleasures?

'Our capacity to change will partly depend on our readiness to face the loss involved. I've often thought that "climate change denial" is a natural emotional response, the first stage of a grieving process. The others – anger, bargaining, depression and acceptance – are an inevitable part of that process. Many of us who have worked with people facing loss or who have faced it in our personal lives will recognise these stages.

'If we can reach an acceptance of the new reality, I believe we can begin to feel hopeful rather than fearful, because there's so much about it that is better than how we live now – more sustainable, peaceful, meaningful and connected to others than our lifestyle up to now.

'I like the idea that the things I enjoy are not exploiting people on the other side of the world or ruining my grandchildren's future.'

**SPECIAL THANKS** TO MY WIFE HELEN FOR THIS INSIGHTFUL PIECE.

REFLECTION

## The thinking

- What's helping me on the ride?
- What's hindering me on the ride?
- How to reduce or remove the hindering factors?

## The action

Summarise any actions here and pencil them into your final plan (see pages 120–125).

CHAPTER 8

*'How did you go bankrupt?' Bill asked. 'Two ways,' Mike said. 'Gradually, then suddenly.'*

*THE SUN ALSO RISES*, ERNEST HEMINGWAY

## Scaling up

Way back near the beginning of this manual I talked about 'scaling up' the human response to a hitherto unimaginable level. We've explored this scaling up in terms of reducing personal pollution and speeding up its impact.

But I've also talked about scaling up as propagation: triggering a massive exponential growth in the number of people actively doing this stuff.

But how on earth do we make this exponential rise happen?

Here's a thought. If at school you learnt about the amoeba, you may remember how it divides into two, and then the two into four, and then the four divides into eight. After nine divisions it gets to over a thousand. That's exponential growth. Why not do that with Carbon Buddy pairs or groups? This would have the huge benefit of bringing new people into the Carbon Buddy community at an exponential rate and quite quickly.

And there's more to it. Many people now have relatives, friends or work colleagues living in other countries. And more and more of them talk to each other using Skype, Zoom, Facetime or Hangouts. Let's use the technology.

Actively drawing in more people is the key to your propagation goal.

And spreading the community to other countries is crucial too.

# The Amoeba Moment

## A metaphor for changing our lifestyles



### A sacrifice for the greater good?

What suddenly struck me like a lightning bolt was the realisation that this apparently simple amoeba moment – **leaving behind something valued, comfortable and familiar, for something (at least initially) less certain and less familiar** – is exactly what we're all going to have to become much better at if we are to change our attitudes, behaviours and lifestyles to leave behind the fossil fuel economy and embrace the low carbon economy.

**Some people tell me this division won't work.** 'Too much of a sacrifice,' they say. 'Why would I want to leave a group that was working well? Why start all over again?'

I can see the problem. For some people it will be more difficult than for others. And I find I both sympathise with it, yet want to challenge the assumptions behind it.

- Yes, there will be a sense of loss. Yes, there will be some disruption to effective and comfortable ways of working. Yes, starting anew will take time.

- It's a yes, too, to new energy, new ideas, new perspectives, new relationships.

- **And the more you do it the more skilful you'll become at managing the bigger transition.** Leaving behind the old and starting anew will become a well-rehearsed routine.

# A fork in the road

## ... the road less travelled?

I'd like to suggest two possible ways in which we might get the exponential growth in numbers and countries that we need. The first is to take a deep breath and give the **dividing route** a go. Become an amoeba and see how it feels.

The second is to follow the **propagating route**. Become a Carbon Buddy propagator and see if that fits you better.

Both these routes, if pursued systematically and persistently, will help us get to where we want to. And of course there's nothing to stop you doing one then the other, or both at the same time, or neither of them.

The table below provides a quick summary of the two routes:

HOW ABOUT?

**Finding** out the best value 100% green electricity tariff

| The **DIVIDING ROUTE** | The **PROPAGATING ROUTE** |
|---|---|
| At the very start, talk with your Carbon Buddy about dividing at some point in the future | Look at your network map to find people who you think might be interested |
| At some point review the possibility of dividing, and decide one way or the other | Or even better, people who you think might be a challenge to persuade |
| If you are in a group, decide how you are going to split ... into pairs or singles or a mixture | Use all your charm and guile to persuade them to find their own Carbon Buddies and start out on their ride together. |
| Each of these then invites one or more new Carbon Buddies to join. Use your network maps to help you find people who will add something. | Or approach a pair of people whom you think will get on and share an interest |
| The new pair or group forms | Tell them where they can buy the manual (or if you're feeling generous give them copies as a present) |
| The 'old lot' become coaches to the 'new lot', helping them to get into it quickly | Keep in touch with them and see if you can help them out at any point, from your experience |

And here's where we need to get to

# Carbon Buddies EVERYWHERE

## We can all play a part in getting there

Here are **some practical things you can do** to help grow the Carbon Buddy Project **rapidly.** The website carbonbuddyproject.org has more details.

1

**WRITE A REVIEW:** one way to nudge others.

Facebook

carbonbuddy project.org

Twitter

2

**SPREAD THE WORD ON SOCIAL MEDIA**

a. **Facebook:** @carbonbuddyproject
b. **Twitter:** @carbonbuddyproj
C. **Instagram:** @carbonbuddyproject_
d. **LinkedIn:** Colin Hastings

3

**VOLUNTEER TO BE A PROPAGATOR:** Make stuff happen in your area

4

**BECOME A DISTRIBUTOR:** special deals to buy some, sell some, give some.

5

**PUT US IN TOUCH WITH ECOPRENEURS:** the emerging cool economy.

6

**YOU HOST A TALK:** we provide a speaker.

7

**JUST TALK TO PEOPLE ABOUT IT:** tell your story to anyone and everyone.

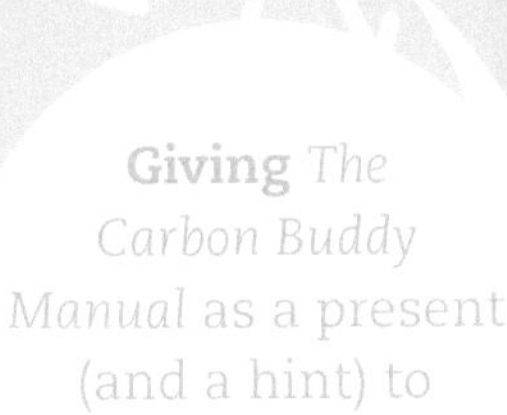


**Giving** *The Carbon Buddy Manual* as a present (and a hint) to friends and family

INTRODUCTION

# Building pressure for change

## It's 'them' that's the problem!

We've looked at a wide range of things that you as an individual can do to reduce your personal pollution. But there are limits to what individuals can do alone. There are many things, not least money and enabling policies, that will need to be provided by national and local governments, international organisations, and businesses. But they are a harder nut to crack.

## Street protest: not for everyone.

Taking to the streets has worked dramatically to raise awareness of **the broad climate change issue** and to get 'them' (and individuals too) to take it more seriously. But it's not for everyone, and it's less good at getting 'them' to focus on the many **specific issues and blockages that need sorting.** How do we do that?

## Campaigning as an individual

You may have never thought of yourself as a campaigner, but if you have a very clear idea of what you want to change and if you really care about it, you can do it. You'll probably find it easier as an individual to campaign on something relatively local to start off with.

- It's easiest to sign petitions. See the website for ways you can do this online.

# Cool power



- The next easiest is to **withdraw your custom from businesses.** But when you do that, make sure you get a message to the business's decision-maker about the fact that you have done so, why you have done so and what your new expectations are. Don't expect them to change yet, though. They will change when you, and enough others like you, have changed.

- The third is to use the power of your vote. **Look at party manifestos,** lobby your MP. If you don't like what you see, then change the way you vote.

- Find local campaign groups.

If you decide to go ahead and do any campaigning yourself or with a local group, the website has some very simple questions that will help you be more effective.

## Get involved with the movers and shakers

But for bigger (though still specific) issues, you need to team up with those who have greater expertise and resources. **There are organisations out there that are expert at influencing.** They have the research, the networks, the training, the credibility and the contacts and know how to get the media onside. Some people call them pressure groups or lobbyists. I like to call them the movers and shakers. They know how to create positive pressure for change. They know the system, the establishment, the decision makers, the corridors of power – all places that most of us find it difficult if not impossible to reach. They are your Trojan horses to bring positive pressure to bear.

# Campaigning
## A civic call for change

### Where to focus your energy

I've already suggested some ways in which you can campaign as an individual. Let's now look a bit more closely at some of the **big but specific issues that will need sorting,** many of them by governments and big businesses. I've made a list of some of the issues I've come across, and it's summarised on the next page. It's not exhaustive; it's meant to provide a starting point for you to decide where you would like to focus your time and effort.

### What businesses need from you

In the case of businesses, as I have already suggested, they won't change unless you're socking it to them that **you have changed** your needs, demands and expectations of them. Tell them that you used to expect all your fruit and veg to be perfectly round but that you have now changed your mind and you don't expect that any more because you don't want to see so much food waste, and so on.

### Why governments need permission from you

We live in an imperfect democracy. Whatever their successes and failings, our local councillors and national politicians are about the only people in the land that receive a performance appraisal every five years which can cost them their jobs. **Climate change is a new challenge, and there is no template of previous experience to draw on.** We need to provide help to those in power through 'a civic call for change' which, if expressed clearly and heard, provides them with guidance for action. Such a call legitimises the changes they make, providing democratic consent for them to be implemented. They need those at the sharp end (that's you and me), to help them navigate their way through the swamp. Many of us understand the swamp better than they do, **so don't just sit and blame them – help them!** I first came across this idea from Paul Allen who heads up the Zero Carbon Britain team at the Centre for Alternative Technology. It gives a different slant to the notion of pressurising for change, and it makes a lot of sense to me.

It is in fact our civic duty to point out to our elected representatives what we need from them in this new territory of climate change. In particular we need to **signal them loud and clear:**

- The main blockages to reducing the sources of our personal pollution that are outside our control.
- The carrots and sticks we would like them to put in place to encourage us – indeed make it possible for us – to do what we need to do.
- The policies, technologies and other resources that need to be put in place to help us do our bit.
- The sacrifices we're prepared to make to fix climate change.

| The focus | Some actions that could be taken | The targets |
|---|---|---|
| Travel and holidays | Limit airport expansion<br>Tax frequent flyers<br>Reduce or stop government subsidies for aviation fuel<br>Introduce regulations requiring the carbon footprint of all package holidays to be shown | Package holiday companies<br>Your national government (Transport Department)<br>Your local politicians |
| Keeping warm and cool | Paid-for nationwide programme of retro-fitting houses with insulation<br>Subsidise modern renewable energy technologies so that they're affordable for everyone<br>All new houses to meet Passivhaus standards | Your national government (Housing, Business, Energy Departments)<br>Your local politicians |
| Personal transport | Enable everyone to purchase an electric car/electric bike<br>Invest in charging infrastructure for charging electric cars<br>Affordable and joined-up public transport<br>Reduce commuting by increasing home/local-based work<br>Invest in cycleways and car-free streets<br>Electric cargo bikes for urban deliveries | Local government<br>Your national government (Transport Department)<br>Your local politicians |
| Food and farming | Laws and incentives to reduce food waste<br>Food miles / carbon footprint info on all food<br>Enable local processing of food waste for energy generation<br>Clean cooking stoves in the majority world<br>Promote a plant-rich diet<br>Shift subsidies away from livestock and towards low carbon plant-based food production<br>Expansion and promotion of local food markets | Supermarkets<br>Your national government (Agriculture, Food Departments)<br>National associations (farming and food) |
| Energy sources | Get a community energy scheme off the ground | Your national government (Housing, Business, Energy Departments)<br>Local government |
| Recreation and events | Create new green spaces for recreation and biodiversity<br>Challenge large sporting and cultural events to recognise, reduce and compensate for their pollution<br>Promote low carbon recreational activities | Local government<br>Event management organisations<br>Large sports clubs<br>Your local politicians |
| Fashion and clothing | Challenge the manufacturing processes and transport chains<br>Make it OK to discuss the whole idea of fashion and what's fashionable | High street fashion stores<br>Fashion-driven consumer groups |
| Natural carbon storage | Help protect tropical and temperate forests<br>Help with conservation/restoration of peatlands<br>Promote growing of bamboo and faster-growing broadleaved trees<br>Promote the idea of environmental growth | Organisations which destroy the natural environment<br>Your national government (Foreign Affairs, International Development Departments)<br>National associations of farming and rural affairs |
| Education and learning | Eat a plant-rich diet including alternative protein sources<br>Family planning<br>Educate all girls in the majority world<br>Make schools healthy eating hubs<br>Provide skills development for the new environmental economy | Educational establishments<br>Your national government (Education, Foreign Affairs, International Development Departments)<br>Your local politicians |

# Volunteering
## Giving your time and commitment

### From local to national to international

I started exploring cool power by looking at different ways of campaigning. I also summarised a wide range of specific issues that need to be resolved if we're to succeed in reaching our Cool Planet Goal, pointing out that to progress along the ride you will almost certainly encounter other blockages which need highlighting and unblocking in some way.

**Rise up now from your local swamp**, and look for a while at the national and even international view. It's really difficult to campaign nationally as an individual. A few Greta Thunbergs or David Attenboroughs achieve it, but they're very special. How, then, can we do this?

### First, identify your preferred movers and shakers

This is where we come to the movers and shakers.

- Make a note below of any organisations you have heard of, and believe are credible, which appear to be working on any of these issues.

- Then take a look at: **carbonbuddy project.org.** There I have made a list of the organisations that I have come across so far. Included in that list are some that I am involved with in some way, but I'm not revealing them, because I don't want to recommend any particular organisation. **It's important for you to make your own judgements and come to your own conclusions** about any you want to get involved with. (It's impossible, though, for me to hide the organisations that have helped me in writing this manual, as I'm honour-bound to acknowledge their help.)

Then see what you can learn from them ...

... and whether you want to go one step further and volunteer to help them.

HOW ABOUT?

**Keeping** a damp flannel in a (multi-use) plastic bag instead of wet wipes

# Donating

HOW ABOUT?

Buying more locally produced food and vegetables

After all that, you may conclude that neither campaigning nor volunteering is going to work for you. In that case you might like to consider setting up a direct debit, to give tangible support to whichever organisation(s) you think fit. If you do, you can often sign up as a member, and get magazines or newsletters packed with good quality reliable information about your chosen issues.

**Draw up a short list of your chosen organisations here:**

| The focus | Movers and shakers | | |
|---|---|---|---|
| | local | national | international |
| Travel and holidays | | | |
| Keeping warm and cool | | | |
| Personal transport | | | |
| Food and farming | | | |
| Energy sources | | | |
| Recreation and events | | | |
| Fashion and clothing | | | |
| Natural carbon storage | | | |
| Education and learning | | | |

REFLECTION

# The thinking

## Which issues do I care most about?

How could I influence these particular issues:

- Directly, and by myself?
- Directly, with a local organisation?
- Indirectly, via a mover and shaker?

Are there any movers and shakers out there:

- That work specifically on the issues I care about?
- That I admire?
- That seem effective?

Might I want to become a member or volunteer?

Or might I prefer to donate?

Or do both?

# The action

Summarise any actions here and pencil them into your final plan as well (see pages 120–125).

CHAPTER

# 10

HOW ABOUT?
?
Ensuring your hot water is at the maximum recommended temperature of 55°C

## INTRODUCTION

# On money ... or the lack of it

We live in a very unequal and very unfair society. The fossil fuel economy over the last half-century has made the disparities in lifestyle between the 'haves' and the 'have nots' even more stark all over the world. I have no doubt that the haves carry a much greater responsibility to use the full range of their resources to drive us towards the Cool Planet Goal. Their lifestyles have created, and still are creating, a disproportionate amount of personal pollution. And they have the means to make a difference. If you see yourself as being lucky enough to be in this privileged group, as do I, one of your key challenges will probably be to overcome the specific sources of inertia associated with wanting to preserve the comforts of the status quo.

If you are one of those citizens who would put yourself in the 'have nots' category, I believe that you have often untapped sources of power that you too can deploy. It is *not* your lot to be a bystander and to feel powerless to influence your grandchildren's futures. I hope this will provide tools to enable you to contribute to this massive project. One of your key challenges will probably be to overcome different kinds of inertia, perhaps to move from believing that you can't do anything to believing that you can.

As I have been writing, I have been trying as hard as I can to hold these two very different audiences in my head and to meet both the sets of needs. Because I count myself fortunate to be a 'have', I do feel a responsibility to play an active part. Luckily for me, the ideas behind the Carbon Buddy Project provide me with a suitable way of doing that. I hope I have sufficient knowledge of and empathy with you if you would describe yourself as a 'have not', and that I have something practical

# Cool spending

## How to use your money to decarbonise just about everything

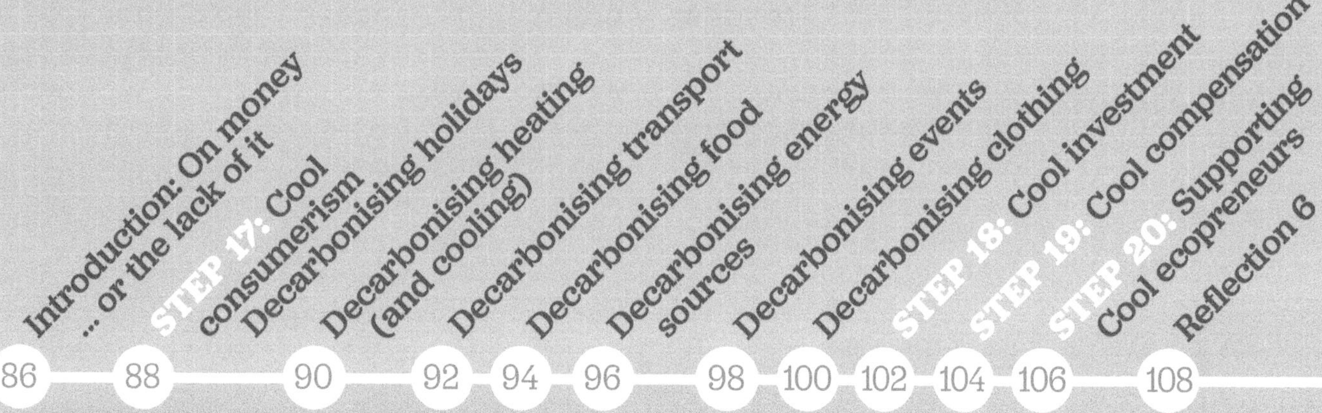


and manageable to offer you. Our original eight strategies may come in useful again here:

1 DOING: we can all find aspects of our personal behaviour and lifestyle to change.

2 CAMPAIGNING: we can all find ways of directly putting pressure on governments and businesses (direct campaigning).

3 VOLUNTEERING: we can all volunteer to help in organisations that have the expertise and power to influence (indirect campaigning and lobbying).

4 LEARNING: we can all widen our understanding of the issues and the solutions (good choice: this manual is not a bad place to start).

5 DONATING: many of us will be able to find money (according to our means) to donate to organisations that have the expertise and power to influence (indirect campaigning and lobbying).

6 SPENDING: many of us will be able to shift our spending patterns towards products and services that help to reach the Cool Planet Goal.

7 INVESTING: a few of us will be able to provide finance for innovation, production and maintenance of emerging carbon reduction technologies.

8 CREATING: a few of us will see and seize opportunities to create new businesses, social enterprises, arts projects, community groups and other relevant ventures.

# Cool consumerism
## Decarbonising holidays

### Dream destinations

So many emotions, hopes and dreams are wound up with holidays and business travel. The marketing muscle of the mass travel industry and the media fuel these emotions to the point that travel and all it **promises have a slightly addictive quality for many.** But not so many years ago, before the advent of low-cost airlines and package holidays, flying was seen as a huge treat. But now, for the young ('everybody's doing it') to the middle-aged ('we need it') and the retired ('we've earned it'), it's now seen more as a right.

### Flying

There are many people who don't fly. Equally there are many who fly occasionally, and there are some who treat a plane like a car. Eurostar say that London to Paris by train emits 4.1 kg of $CO_2$ per passenger whereas flying emits 63.6 kg. Check out the numbers if you like. Just one flight can wipe out all the hard-earned $CO_2$ reductions you've made by other methods. **I'm sorry to say it, but flying is the big one.**

### More enjoyable alternatives?

I'm trying hard to cut out flying, to imagine life without flying. I've learned a lot from recent experimental trips with Brava, my folding bike (I introduced you to her on page 10), as I experiment with different types of transport and different concepts of travel and holidays.

- The internet and smartphone apps have transformed booking and tracking trains.
- Mobile phone apps have taken much of the anxiety out of booking a bed for the night at short notice, leaving room for more spontaneity.
- Even though I'm quite a shy sort of guy when travelling, I've had some wonderful interactions with strangers as I ride along on my bike. I connect with people in a quite different way.
- Think about the wonderful places to be visited without flying which are within 500 miles of where you live and how you might reach them by train, coach, car, boat, bicycle … or on foot!
- An overland or water-based journey is usually a joy in itself, infinitely more pleasurable, interesting and relaxing than flying.
- There is huge fun to be had in the advance planning … but equally there is fun to be had in **not** planning as you go along!
- **The destination is less important than the getting there.** And for many, getting there by plane is no longer a pleasure.

### The way forward?

**Reducing or even stopping flying:** there's a growing movement in Sweden, called Flygskam (flight-shaming), of people who are giving up flying. So

successful has its uptake been that passenger numbers have dropped by 8% in Swedish airports in 2019.

Thoughts of giving up or reducing flying may at first be put into the 'sacrifice' or 'too difficult' box. That is to say that **the mindset is all about what is 'lost'.** But what it ignores is what is gained. And I think there is a lot to be put on the credit side by reimagining what it is to travel, and what travel really means. Not flying doesn't have to mean not travelling.

## Experiment with different ways of travelling

It's simple. **Think rail, ferry, sail, car, coach, pedal bike, e-bike and walking** (and particularly how to combine them).

## Telepresence

Improved communication technologies such as Zoom and Skype make some business journeys unnecessary, although there is a danger of the rebound effect, where people make friends online and then want to go and meet them face to face.

I am fascinated by the idea of virtual tourism growing out of virtual reality technology. I imagine my local guide in, say, India, Tanzania or Peru. They have a special camera linked to a satellite which is livestreaming to me in the comfort of my home. Before we set off, I pay my guide with one click from my smartphone to theirs. We tour the sites (which are relatively empty of people, so we can really see them properly, and they – and we! – don't suffer the collateral damage of overtourism), chatting as we go along. The guide stops occasionally, and we have conversations with local people along the way. In time, too, the guide will be able to transmit the smells on the trip which are such an evocative part of travel. **How cool is all that? And with no personal pollution.** Another challenge for our ecopreneurs!

## Flights as treats

John Vidal, a respected travel writer, has been experimenting with and writing about a flight-free life. His conclusion is 'if we are to fly it should only be for truly extraordinary reasons'.

## What about sunshine and warmth?

No problem. If things go on as they are, hot countries will become too hot, **and the current cooler countries will become the warm ones.** Job done!

**ACTION** ZONE

- Have a play on ecopassenger.org to compare the carbon impact of different modes of transport for different journeys.
- If there are more than two of you, driving may be the best for some trips. But take the bike as well!
- Google 'slow travel manifesto Hidden Europe'.
- Think travel long-haul virtually and short-haul actually.
- Try a flight-free year and see how it goes.
- When comparing flights with other means of transport, remember to compare the full cost (and time) of getting door to door. Ensure you add in luggage, booked seats, travel delays, strikes, airport transfers, car parking etc.

# Decarbonising heating (and cooling)

## Winter heating is one of the 'big ones' in colder climates. Air conditioning is likewise one of the 'big ones' in warmer climates

In an average house, **about two-thirds of all energy used in cold climates is for heating.** Same goes for aircon in hot climates. Globally these domestic sources of energy consumption are massive.

Meeting our currently high heating and aircon demand with only renewable energy sources may be difficult. As most of our existing homes are going to be around for a long while, **we need to start working out how to reduce their heating/cooling demand** so that a low carbon solution is possible.

## Heat loss can be radically reduced

The main steps are to add good draught-proofing, increase insulation, and provide adequate ventilation without causing heat loss. By properly insulating the walls, roof and floor, upgrading windows and doors, and improving air-tightness, heat loss can be halved. Further savings come through better heating controls, so you only heat rooms to the temperature required when they are in use.

Draught-proofing is often a simple low-cost DIY job that you can do whether you own or rent your home. A well draught-proofed house still feels comfortable at a slightly lower temperature. Make sure you still provide adequate, but controlled, ventilation.

If possible it's better to choose insulation materials that have not been heavily processed as this will reduce your personal pollution and environmental impact. These natural, plant-based materials, such as wood-fibre board or hemp, also sequester carbon into the building fabric. However, these are not as widely available, and it's far better to install cheaper and locally available synthetic insulation (if appropriate to the application) than nothing at all. Using these natural insulations can be important for an older house, where the 'breathability' of the building fabric must be maintained.

The links on the website give more detail on the techniques and materials that can be used to insulate a house, including older houses with solid walls. The latter are more difficult to insulate, but the savings can be substantial.

For a new building designed to a very high standard (e.g. Passivhaus), triple glazing is best, but good quality double glazing is likely to be most appropriate for a balanced refurbishment of an existing home. Glazing panes with an argon-fill and 'low-e' coating are the most efficient. The manufacture of timber-framed windows has a much lower environmental impact than that of uPVC or aluminium.

When very good air-tightness can be achieved, heat-recovery ventilation can be used to extract heat from the outgoing stale air in order to warm up the incoming fresh air. For an existing house, single-room heat recovery ventilation can be effective for a bathroom or kitchen, to retain heat when extracting steam and smells.

## And what about cooling??

Improved insulation and draught-proofing also helps reduce the overheating of buildings in summer by keeping the heat out and maintaining a cool indoor temperature. To allow this to work you also need to avoid internal heat gains, and ventilate the building at night with cooler air. A building that has good internal mass (exposed solid floor or walls) will be easier to keep cool. Depending on the size and orientation of glazing, some additional shading, such as an awning, shutters or exterior solar shade, may be important.

## A glimpse of what's possible

If building a new house, or doing a very extensive renovation, going beyond the current building regulations is vital for future-proofing a home. Building to the Passivhaus standard will create a house with a heating demand that's about 10% of the current average.

**SPECIAL THANKS** TO JOEL RAWSON, CAT CENTRE FOR ALTERNATIVE TECHNOLOGY

### ACTION ZONE

- Draught-proof doors and windows.
- Insulate all parts of your home – including the floor – as thoroughly as possible.
- Install good heating controls and set a *maximum* of 19°C. In winter wear a jumper, and warm slippers!
- If the air in and around your house is damp – and especially if it's prone to mould – get a dehumidifier. It uses very little electricity, you'll feel warmer at a lower temperature, and you're less likely to suffer from mould- and damp-related complaints.
- To help keep your home cool in summer, install awnings, or exterior blinds or shutters, on windows that face the sun. People living in hot countries have understood these technologies for centuries.
- Consider heat-recovery ventilation in key rooms.
- If your budget limits what you can do, join up with others to campaign for better local or national support for energy-saving refurbishment.

STEP 17

# Cool consumerism

## Decarbonising transport

### The legacy of the internal combustion engine

Taking the UK as an example, transport is one of the main causes of our climate change problem, as it is responsible for **about a quarter of our greenhouse gas emissions.**

Due to the low efficiency of many vehicles, transport accounts for a larger proportion of overall energy use in the UK – about 40%. Within that total, about 55% is for passenger vehicles, 20% for aviation and 25% for freight.

On average, a British person travels around 6,500 miles a year by car or van, with this accounting for about half of all energy used in transport. In the 1950s and '60s, most households did not own a car, and travel by bicycle and bus was at much higher levels than today. But since then the car has become an addictive symbol of freedom, convenience, autonomy, glamour and status. A similar conundrum applies worldwide and will get worse as the majority world, understandably, demands the same standard of living as the rich nations.

### The emerging technologies are here, now

Electric cars and buses are around three times as efficient as new vehicles that run on petrol or diesel – and they are up to six or seven times as efficient as the average vehicle on the road in 2019. Electric cargo bikes could have a significant role in deliveries within urban areas. Electric cars are leading to lower carbon emissions, even with the current mixture of energy sources feeding our electricity grid. As we move towards a zero-carbon grid, emissions from charging electric vehicles should gradually drop to zero. **An overall reduction in individual car use is still important, though, in order to make it possible to meet the energy demand with only renewable energy.**

The range of electric vehicles is increasing all the time, with the biggest advances in efficiency sometimes coming from less well-known brands. As the average journey length is only seven miles, and around 90% of car journeys made by cars are less than 100 miles, very few journeys will need to involve recharging en route. In addition, the availability of second-hand electric cars is increasing, making them more affordable to a wider public. Older vehicles with shorter ranges will become particularly attractive to people with less money, who mostly drive relatively short distances.

### The healthy option

Moving back to more walking, cycling, and use of public transport is the best way to reduce our energy demand and greenhouse gas emissions. As this will lead to less traffic, it will also make our living environments more pleasant and healthy. E-bikes in particular have huge potential not only environmentally but also in health benefits. Owners tend to ride much further with an e-bike than a standard one, and get better quality cardio exercise, putting less strain on the heart. I've just got one and it's fantastic. Like riding on a magic carpet!

By arranging carsharing, either informally or via carshare schemes, the average occupancy of cars could improve from the current average of 1.6 people per vehicle. Modern communication technology makes it much easier to arrange lift shares to work, or sign up to a local car club. And you get to chat to people and make friends en route.

**SPECIAL THANKS** TO JOEL RAWSON, CAT CENTRE FOR ALTERNATIVE TECHNOLOGY

*I am the traffic.*

JONATHAN MILLER

## **ACTION** ZONE

- Walk and cycle more when possible – perhaps with an electric bike to boost range.
- Reduce car use by using public transport and carsharing schemes.
- Switch to an electric vehicle. But do your research carefully first. Take a look at the Information Gateway on the website for more on this.
- Get involved in local campaigns to improve infrastructure for all the above changes.

# Cool consumerism
## Decarbonising food

### Three dodgy gases

**Throughout the world , local agricultural food production is a very significant source of total greenhouse gas (GHG) emissions.** Some of this is carbon dioxide, but a lot is either methane or nitrous oxide, both of which – by volume – have a much bigger effect on the climate than carbon dioxide.

Because consumers in many countries also eat a lot of imported foods, they're indirectly responsible for GHG emissions from agriculture and land use changes in other countries, as well as the emissions involved in getting produce to their tables. These overseas carbon emissions could be as much again as those within countries, but it is hard to get accurate figures. Livestock products are often the key problem, for example clearing rainforest in order to rear cattle or to grow animal feed for export to other countries.

Direct carbon dioxide emissions come from energy use by agricultural machinery, food processing and transport. Energy efficiency measures and renewable energy can be used to decarbonise.

### Livestock

However, a very large proportion of agricultural GHG emissions are from methane and nitrous oxide. These can be harder to reduce because they're mainly from biological sources. For example, methane makes up over 30% of agricultural GHG emissions in the UK. **It's mainly burped out by cows and sheep as they digest grass** (by enteric fermentation). Some methane also comes from animal manure.

When fertilisers are used, not all the nitrogen they contain is taken up by the crop. **Some fertiliser gets broken down by bacteria in the soil, releasing large quantities of nitrous oxide ($N_2O$).** Some of this is from land used in the production of crops we eat ourselves, but in many countries as much land is used to grow animal feed. So although pigs and chickens don't release methane, $N_2O$ emissions arise from the production of their food.

### How best to get our protein?

Producing protein from meat requires a lot more land and fertiliser inputs than growing an equivalent amount of plant-based protein. Savings of both methane and nitrous oxide emissions mean that a **diet high in plant protein** (such as beans, legumes, cereals and vegetables) will lead to much lower greenhouse gas emissions.

Eating a low-meat diet is also good for our health. At the moment, an average Western diet has a far higher energy content than we actually need to satisfy our daily activities and basic metabolic processes. There are also health impacts

> *If we can't picture ourselves in the solution, we will surely stay stuck in the problem.*
>
> PAUL ALLEN AND CATRIONA TOMS, CENTRE FOR ALTERNATIVE TECHNOLOGY

from highly processed meats, and other processed foods loaded with fat, sugar and salt. A low carbon diet, based on fresh foods and wholegrains, will help to lower the rate of diet-related diseases.

## More than we need

When our dietary energy intake exceeds our needs, some of the energy and carbon involved in food production is effectively wasted. **More direct waste occurs with the food that is thrown away at home, in the supply chain and at the farm.** Reducing this waste is also very important to help reduce carbon emissions.

## Using land wisely

If we eat less meat, related benefits will arise from much less grazing land and cropland being required, allowing us **to encourage land-based livelihoods based on non-food crops.** This could include growing various grasses, coppiced wood and forestry to produce carbon-sequestering building materials and the raw materials for making synthetic renewable fuels. It would also allow the restoration of peatland and unharvested woodland, both of which help absorb excess carbon emissions while promoting biodiversity.

**SPECIAL THANKS** TO JOEL RAWSON, CAT CENTRE FOR ALTERNATIVE TECHNOLOGY

### **ACTION** ZONE

- Move to a low-meat, low-dairy diet with more plant-based protein (eg beans, peas, lentils).
- Avoid very processed foods, such as those high in fats, sugar and salt, and plan a healthy diet (wholegrains, fresh veg and fruit etc).
- Minimise food waste.
- Get involved in the wider issues around greenhouse gas emissions from land use and agriculture – eg perhaps a local awareness-raising campaign.
- Consider also the ethical and social issues when choosing between brands/suppliers.

# Cool consumerism
## Decarbonising energy sources

### Use less energy

Our use of fossil fuels is the main cause of climate change, and so moving to renewable energy sources is vital.

**Saving energy is always the first step.** Energy-saving lighting and appliances are now widely available, offering substantial savings on electricity use and carbon emissions. Check up on energy labels, as the best possible ratings vary between appliances. Domestic lighting needs can be met with compact fluorescent lamps (CFLs) or LEDs. A modern electric induction hob gives the controllability and efficiency of gas, but can use renewable electricity.

### Use green energy

Signing up for a green tariff from a company focused only on renewable energy is an important but easy way to support the renewable energy industry, because the money from your bills funds further development of renewable energy. **But you still need to keep reducing energy use!**

Beyond that, consider investing in a community-owned energy project – or even get involved in setting one up if you can. If you rent or live in a building where putting in your own solar panels is not possible, investing in a community scheme means you'll still have a share in the carbon savings and financial benefits from renewable energy.

Many of the best renewable energy sources (such as wind, wave and tidal power) involve large-scale installations, often away from towns and cities. However, community ownership still allows local people to have a stake in these projects.

**Windpower and other renewable energy sources are not usually feasible at household level,** but domestic solar photovoltaic (PV) panels are an effective way of generating renewable electricity. You may generate more electricity than you use on a sunny day in summer and almost certainly less than you need in winter, so an arrangement to import and export as necessary will help balance your other renewable energy sources in a potentially zero carbon grid.

### Solar hot water

A solar thermal system is used to heat water for bathroom and kitchen. About **1 square metre of tubes per person can supply about 60% of their hot water needs.** A combination of both types of solar panel will give the biggest contribution of energy per square metre from a given roof area. Solar water heating can also supplement a main central heating system.

## Heat pumps

As we move towards a zero-carbon grid, we could use electricity to power heat pumps instead of gas boilers to heat our homes. Air or ground source heat pumps extract some heat, at a comparatively low temperature, from the outside air or the ground and use an electric compressor to convert this large amount of low-temperature energy into a smaller amount of medium-temperature energy, warming the building.

In some situations, 'air to air' heating (and cooling) units might be a more practical alternative. They heat air (but not water) using reverse refrigeration. Sounds strange but it's pretty efficient. Refrigeration (rather than renewables) engineers sell them.

## Biomass boilers

**For some old houses that are hard to insulate,** some form of wood-fired (biomass) heating may be more appropriate than a heat pump. An automated boiler can burn compressed sawdust pellets very efficiently and cleanly, without the smoky emissions from some conventional wood-burning appliances. However, as the land for growing wood fuel is limited in many countries, biomass is not a universal solution.

**SPECIAL THANKS** TO JOEL RAWSON, CAT CENTRE FOR ALTERNATIVE TECHNOLOGY

### **ACTION** ZONE

- Upgrade to energy-efficient lighting and appliances.
- Support renewable energy by purchasing from an ethical and low-carbon supplier.
- Invest in (or help set up) a local community-owned energy scheme.
- Install domestic solar panels – photovoltaic or water-heating (or both).
- Move to a heat pump for heating (alongside insulation improvements), or perhaps biomass if appropriate.
- Keep an eye open for developments in the use of hydrogen as an energy source. It's a way off, but likely to accelerate fast.

# Cool consumerism
## Decarbonising events

### Some things become undiscussable

Things become undiscussable when everyone knows about them yet they seem too difficult to address: 'This is where I'm going to lose some friends.' **'This is where I'm going to struggle between what my heart says and what my head says.'** 'This is where I can't win whatever I say!'

### My lightbulb moment

One of my lightbulb moments was when Mike Berners-Lee in his book *How Bad are Bananas* (1st edition 2010) put **the 2010 Football World Cup in South Africa in his highest (1 million tonnes of $CO_2$+) category of emissions.** That made me think. And dig a bit deeper.

HOW ABOUT?

Asking yourself 'how much is enough?'

### Mega events: a few numbers

- The average attendance at a UK premier league football match is about 40,000 people. Of the home supporters, many will walk or come by public transport. Some will come by car. Away supporters may come by train or car, but some will travel longer distances by air.

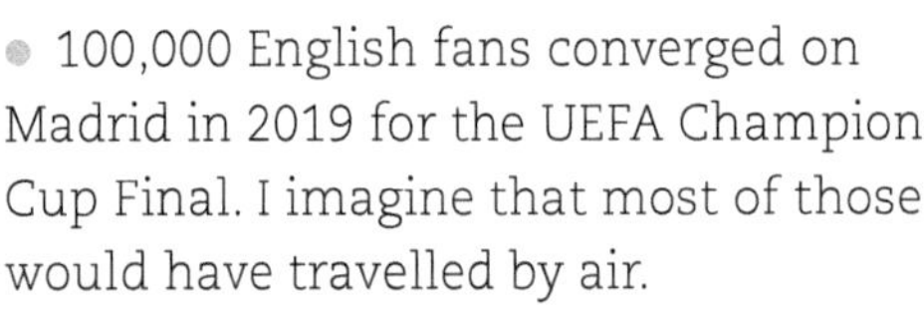

- 100,000 English fans converged on Madrid in 2019 for the UEFA Champions Cup Final. I imagine that most of those would have travelled by air.

- The 2012 London Olympics and Paralympics attracted 471,000 visitors from overseas. Again, I can guess that most of those would have travelled by air, though some would have travelled by train from the near continent.

Around 600,000 international visitors attended the 2019 Rugby World Cup in Japan. I think it's safe to assume that **nearly all of those will have travelled by air.**

Add to the air travel the carbon emissions associated with building new stadiums, hotels, car parks and food outlets. Add to that the sanitation, rubbish, food waste and floodlights.

Look around the internet and it's difficult to find much about this particular climate change issue. The World Rugby website gives us a clue why: this is all about **big** money. Some of the event organisers spout 'sustainability'. They give advice to fans about the simple things that they can do. But they avoid the big one: the mass air travel.

### Micro-events

If you have read the small print earlier, you will know that my Italian class had an important role in micro events. On one occasion, a member of the class described how her daughter's plans for her wedding were getting more and more elaborate, and more and more expensive. And then she paused ... and suddenly realised that **the personal pollution of the wedding was mushrooming,** too.

'I'm going to suggest to my daughter that she has a low-carbon wedding,' she said, only half-joking.

That led naturally to a discussion about hen and stag parties, where the whole party flies off to some exotic location for a short break. One group I heard about went from Europe to Hong Kong for the *weekend*. And that in turn led me to think about conferences. I had an ironic conversation with a strongly climate-activist friend who was an academic. For him, going to conferences was a self-evident good. I rapidly realised that suggesting any other option was probably undiscussable.

## Party pooper!

Yes, I know. Why would I ever want to cast doubt on events which bring such joy to thousands who attend, and millions who watch on TV? Why would I want to open up difficult conversations about issues that seem irresolvable? **Why *shouldn't* people fly miles to have fun?** Why *shouldn't* couples invite huge numbers from far and wide to their extended wedding celebrations? Well, by now you know the answer, and so do I.

## A way forward?

There is some good news. In all areas there will be pathfinders who suddenly decide that enough is enough and that something has to change. One such is the Glastonbury Festival. The organisers made a big move in 2019 by banning single use plastic bottles on the site for all 200,000 festival goers, performers and staff. Credit where credit is due; **the organisers are using their power to challenge and change attitudes** and behaviour.

Perhaps this gives us a clue about how we could begin to chip away at this undiscussable problem. See the Action Zone below for a few suggestions.

### ACTION ZONE

- Approach event organisers sensitively and informally, to raise their awareness of the issues.
- Put pressure on event management companies and ticket sellers to take some responsibility for the environmental consequences of their business model.
- Someone needs to invent a tool that enables mega and micro event organisers to calculate the carbon footprint of events. Come on, you ecopreneurs!
- Draw the attention of event organisers to my conclusions (see pages 104–105) on carbon compensation. There is big money here, and a lot of it ought to be going into new carbon emissions reduction projects. Not just tokenism.

HOW ABOUT?

**Challenging** unnecessarily large portions in fast food joints and restaurants.

Thinking of the undiscussable ... do I have any friends left?

# Cool consumerism
## Decarbonising clothing

### Clothing and fashion: the hidden story

In 2018 my wife and I went to an exhibition at the Victoria and Albert Museum in London called 'Fashioned from Nature'. Wow! Not only was it visually stunning but also it was an eye-opener; I had never realised quite **how much the fashion and clothing industry contributed to carbon emissions.**

### Some facts about the clothing industry

A recent report by the respected Ellen MacArthur Foundation came up with some gob-smacking facts:

- The textile industry emits more greenhouse gases each year than all international flights and maritime shipping combined.
- The relative impact from fashion is forecast to increase significantly: at current rates, it could account for **over 25% of the global carbon budget by 2050.**
- Looking at the different stages of the supply chain that have an impact on climate, fibre production is responsible for 17% of it; fabric production 42%; garment production 11%; distribution and retail 4%; consumer transportation 23%; and laundry 3%.

Even the growing of natural fibres is problematic, with cotton in particular in the spotlight. But man-made fibres derived from fossil fuel sources also are part of the problem. Oil-derived synthetics such as polyester not only contribute to greenhouse gas emissions, but also generate microplastic pollution of rivers, lakes and oceans, threatening marine organisms and ultimately human health. It is estimated that 35% of the microplastics which end up in the oceans come from synthetic clothing.

### Fast fashion

Consumption of so-called mass fast fashion is driven by a mixture of low price and social **pressure to be seen in the latest fashion statement.** The 'latest' can now change monthly, some big chains releasing 12 new collections a year, with the result that much fast fashion is seen as disposable.

### Practical clothing

But in addition to clothing as fashion, clothing for practical protection and comfort will become increasingly important as our climate changes. We will need to wear warmer clothing indoors as we reduce the temperatures inside. And rather than buying different clothes for summer or going on holiday, perhaps the core of our wardrobe will stay the same year-round (essentially summer garments) with additional layering next to the skin and on top to provide the added warmth and comfort in winter.

This provides an intriguing challenge to the clothing industry. In the past the fashionistas have held practical clothing in contempt, and the practical types have equally stared with amazement at the impractical outfits worn by those in the latest fashions. In the new world of the green economy, **fast fashion may be looked back on as a quaint relic of the fossil fuel economy.** Rather than having the latest thing, perhaps consumers will become much more concerned to have clothing that works better and lasts longer.

## Innovations in the garment business

One positive thing that the fashion industry has in abundance is creativity, and this is being turned towards the wider challenge of reducing the industry's carbon footprint. New processes and uses are being found for natural fibres such as hemp, jute, bamboo and sisal. There is innovation in **creating garments from the most unlikely of source materials** such as grape and citrus waste, and pineapple fibre. New research is coming up with ways of creating the same chemical building blocks as those provided by oil, but deriving them instead from natural fibrous plants that grow on marginal land that is unsuitable for food production. This holds the promise of high tech clothing with good warming, cooling and waterproofing qualities, and with much lower carbon footprints and no microplastic pollution.

## The new cool: clothing without fashion

But even if the overall carbon footprint of the production process is reduced, we still have those drivers of cheapness, constant new lines and peer and media pressure in place. There's still a lot of stuff being bought and swiftly thrown away.

But those drivers are being challenged. Instead of it being cool to have the latest, it will hopefully become cool to buy second-hand, to mend, to buy better quality and keep it longer. **Will the new cool consumers send a message to the big retailers, stopping the treadmill?** Will new start-ups begin to provide the new cool low carbon fashion offering? Yes!

**SPECIAL THANKS** TO ANNA BRISMAR OF GREEN STRATEGY SWEDEN.

HOW ABOUT?

**Making** a list of all the things you dispose of in a week

## **ACTION** ZONE

- Ask shop assistants to find out, and tell you, what their companies are doing to reduce the carbon footprint of their products.
- Buy second-hand. Take your unwanted and saleable clothes to a charity shop.
- Learn how to sew and work with fabric. That way you can not only mend clothes, but buy used ones and use your creativity to turn them into new clothes.
- Rent clothes for special occasions.
- Have a clothes-exchange party with a bunch of friends.
- Check the default temperature of your washing machine. It may be washing at a higher temperature than necessary; 30°C will do fine for many items.
- Don't buy new latest fad branded fancy dress kits for kids. Get them involved in creating their very own 'designer' fancy dress outfits from old clothes and other materials.
- Take your worn-out garments and shoes to clothes banks or recycling stations for fabric recycling.
- Give away unwanted garments to relatives, friends, neighbours.
- If possible, buy clothes of high quality and more timeless design to make your wardrobe last longer in both quality and style.

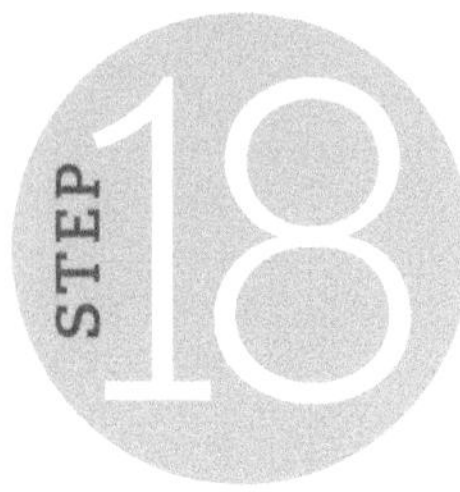


# Cool investment
## Decarbonising investment

### What is cool investment?

Investment has always been about maximising profit. But increasingly it also demands a wider sense of purpose. Cool investment is all about shifting your investments away from fossil fuel-based assets and towards immediate carbon reduction technologies and services.

**Investing** in seaweed production. Good for fish and good for $CO_2$ absorption

The financial world has been slow to see carbon reduction as an investment opportunity. There have been many investment funds sporting eco or green or ESG (Environmental, Social and Governance) credentials – but their remit is more about so-called ethical investment. This approach suggests that much more targeted finance is required to accelerate the development and sale of **technologies that produce significant and rapid reductions in carbon emissions,** or that have the potential to do so.

### New proven mainstream technologies

Some of the technologies are now mature. Others are still in the start-up phase. Most financial advisers will be cautious, but don't be put off. There are certainly collective 'themed' funds out there that focus on the new and emerging environmental technologies and services, which have a good performance track record, and will not raise the risks in your portfolio.

### Pressure from financial regulators

The good news on a macro scale is that governments and the wider financial regulators are now pushing for change. The Norway Sovereign Wealth Fund has recently divested many of its holdings in oil and gas exploration. In 2017, 34 central banks and supervisors – representing five continents, half of global greenhouse gas emissions and the supervision of two-thirds of the global systemically important banks and insurers – joined forces to create a coalition of the willing: the Network for Greening the Financial System (NGFS).

The Governors of the Bank of England and the Bank of France presented the NGFS first report stating: 'Supervisors are encouraged to set expectations to ensure financial firms are adequately addressing the financial risks from climate change, including by conducting scenario analysis to **assess their strategic resilience to climate change policy.** Firms are encouraged to take a long-term, strategic approach to the consideration of these risks, and to embed them into their business-as-usual governance and risk-management frameworks.' The investment industry and regulators worldwide are all beginning to take significant new steps in this direction. The pressure for climate change action is clearly increasing and will continue to increase substantially. Thus the demand for the key technologies will also increase.

## Where does the money come from?

Finding the money to bring these new technologies and services to market at scale is a massive challenge, as is paying for them to deployed on a huge scale. The last IPCC (Intergovernmental Panel on Climate Change) report talked of mouth-wateringly large sums which are pretty nigh incomprehensible to folks like me. Anyway, it's **a lot.**

One school of thought is that there is plenty of money in the international financial system for the task ahead – but it's just in the wrong places!

| Away from | Towards |
|---|---|
| Fossil fuels | Offshore and onshore wind energy |
| Supermarkets | Solar farms |
| Processed food | Low carbon transportation |
| Single-use plastics | Low carbon travel |
| Agribusiness | Sustainable packaging |
| Concrete manufacturing | Low carbon building materials |
| | Sustainable architecture |
| | Low carbon food production |
| | Low carbon food distribution |
| | Eliminating food waste |
| | Recycling |
| | High-capacity renewable energy storage |
| | Virtual tourism |
| | New skills for the future environmental economy |

This is fine for the big guns. But at the other end of the spectrum we should be equally aware of financing needs of the many **new start-up businesses and social enterprises** that will grow out of the opportunities offered by the emerging green economy. These are the new ecopreneurs who will become an increasingly visible part of the landscape, offering new products and services to the new cool consumers. Start-up money is notoriously difficult to come by, so they will appreciate any help going.

We also need to recognise that initiatives will spring out of local communities. Likewise, it can be very difficult for them to raise money for their schemes.

I'll offer suggestions how both these sectors might access suitable finance in the next section, Step 19: Cool compensation (see pages 104–105).

### ACTION ZONE

- Try instructing those who invest your money, or lobbying those who manage your pension funds, to withdraw money from high carbon emissions sectors, and to shift it towards the new high growth / low carbon sectors.
- If they seem resistant (or ignorant) at first, keep pressing.
- If they still don't respond, be prepared to change to professionals whose views are more in line with your own.

# Cool compensation
## Decarbonising everything else

### Guilt or what?

I've never been a great one for guilt. Not a very useful emotion, in my book. But right through this ride, I've had a niggly feeling that has just refused to go away. I locked it away. Time to let it speak.

My problem is this. I feel good about all the work that we have done on our ride to cut down on our personal pollution. **But I can't seem to get out of my head the fact that we will inevitably continue to cause some pollution.** Worse still, I can still 'see' my historical pollution – all that stuff I spewed out and the damage it caused before I started on this ride. And I can't help thinking that I still have some responsibility for clearing that up. But how to exercise that responsibility? Who pays to clear up or mitigate this particular pollution?

### Language

I begin to think about what my objective is. Words wander around in my mind: payback, offsetting, compensation, reparations, sequestration, repairing, reclaiming. I settle on 'compensation' (for no other good reason than it starts with a 'c' and alliterates with 'cool', a theme you will now be very familiar with).

### Five key principles

How might we compensate for our historical and residual pollution? There are a few principles we might follow:

- THE POLLUTER PAYS: already a well-established principle in pollution management. But let's not wriggle out of our responsibilities with a neat sleight of hand that many fall for. It's common to hear people saying 'Why bother? They [*it's most often China that's cited*] are still going on polluting.' Remember this: a **very large part of what WE consume** is manufactured for us in those countries. Much of their pollution is created in making our products – and in disposing of our rubbish. **THEIR pollution is actually OUR pollution.** And, just to ram the point home, without China's world-beating capability in developing and manufacturing cheap solar panels, the world would not have been able to deploy this ground-breaking technology as rapidly and cheaply as now.

- TARGETED: by now you will be familiar with our priority solutions for creating huge and rapid reductions in carbon emissions. **Those same targets should be guiding us in developing a compensation plan.**

- REGULARITY: because our residual pollution is ongoing, I believe our compensation payments need to be ongoing as well. For me, that means beginning to **think of them as part of our regular household expenditure,** like electricity, broadband, or mobile phone bills. These payments could be made at the standard rates used by the carbon offset organisations. I'm on the lookout for ways of doing this by monthly standing order.

- PROPORTIONAL: the overall pollution of those of us who have been around longer is inevitably larger. How about this formula, then? Take the standard offset rate multiplied by the average number of tonnes per year of your historical pollution. Then multiply the standard rate by the **number of decades you have enjoyed on the planet.**

- INTERNATIONAL: early on in our ride, I wrote this paragraph, and I repeat it here as it says it all: *The consequences of our lifestyles here produce tangible effects there. The consequences of what is happening there will affect us here. And saying that 'there' has to take all the mitigating action misunderstands how the physics and the world is interconnected. Action has to be taken everywhere.*

In looking for ways to pay compensation for our historical and residual pollution, **we need to look for opportunities to support the deployment of our targeted solutions anywhere in the world,** and not just on our doorsteps.

## A word about carbon offset

If you already know about carbon offset, you might be saying, 'Isn't this just carbon offset?' Yes and no. Carbon offset can meet some of the five principles, but not all. And it is not without controversy. But it provides a starting point to an approach which meets all five principles. **I don't think that approach yet exists,** so we will need in the meantime to fall back on my favourite strategy of the good enough.

## What else is available?

In recent years there have been a number of innovations in the ways in which individuals can help finance carbon reduction projects around the world. These include **new types of crowdfunding, new community bonds and share issues, renewable energy cooperatives, carbon offset schemes, and ethical investment platforms.** The options are too detailed to describe here. To help you make up your mind, you will find specific options (**not** recommendations) and much more information on the website. There two broad approaches:

- Financial gateways: these provide the individual with a route into relevant projects.

- Ecopreneur start-ups: a bit more difficult to find, I suspect, but they're out there.

## The small print

When you start looking at these options, **bear in mind that almost all of them will have an element of financial risk** greater than putting your money into a building society. However, many of them are regulated in some way or other, either internationally (for example, the UN Gold Standard for Carbon Offset Projects) or by financial regulators in different countries.

# Cool ecopreneurs
## Decarbonising business

Many years ago I knew a Swedish business professor who **described an entrepreneur as 'a dreamer who does'.** I like that. It encapsulates the mixture of imagination and practicality that such people have. Then the word 'social entrepreneur' entered the management jargon. These were people who started up businesses that mixed the pursuit of profit with the desire to make a positive social impact.

'Profit with a purpose' was the phrase used by some to describe that philosophy. In a former incarnation I had a crack at being a social entrepreneur and **I know at first hand how incredibly difficult it is.** I got to know several social entrepreneurs at that time, and all of them were admirable human beings, passionately driven by the desire to make a difference to people's lives. I really admire them.

### What's an ecopreneur?

Someone came up with the word 'eco-preneur' to describe the risk-takers who are creating new products and services for the new green economy. I'm not sure it's my favourite word, but the alternative, environmental entrepreneur, is a bit of a mouthful. So ecopreneur it will be.

### Gutsy people living the new dream

These ecopreneurs are the people who understand the environmental challenges and see them not as barriers but as opportunities. Yes, big business has a huge responsibility to reduce its carbon footprint. Most companies will do that, sooner or later. A few are run by cynical laggards who will be forced to follow.

I want to highlight ecopreneurs here because they are a **powerful antidote to the general gloom and negativity** around climate change. They think positively, and they give us hope. And they are run by real people who we can go along and meet, and talk to and learn from. I admire these pathfinders hugely, and I want to play my part in making them more visible and celebrating what they're doing.

### The need for patient finance

I have also suggested elsewhere (see Cool compensation pages 104–105) that those who might fancy a bit of an investment punt might consider helping to finance an ecopreneurial start-up. **Sympathetic and patient backers are a lifeline to budding ecopreneurs.** Patient backers are more understanding and less demanding than whose who provide traditional venture capital finance; the patient investor is motivated as much by getting a social or environmental return as a financial return. Getting into providing patient finance is definitely not for everyone, and needs **to be entered into knowingly,** but it's a great way to creating a wider environmental impact with your money if you are fortunate enough to be in a position to do so.

## Making ecopreneurs visible

I want to find ways of highlighting and publicising these pathfinder businesses. Let's just start by buying their products, telling other people about them and promoting them on social media. This will take time. But you can help to build it more quickly by seeking out these types of enterprise in your local area and beyond. Then let me know about the ones you really like and I'll find ways to spread the word. Hopefully that will eventually serve both as a way to find such products and services in a particular area and also even to provide inspiration for new ecopreneurial start-ups.

Below you'll find a few examples of ecopreneurial businesses that I have either come across or heard about, together with one or two wildcard ideas that have come to me on my ride. It's a pretty random sample. Let's build on this.

| | |
|---|---|
| A **market gardener** growing organic vegetables and boxing them up for delivery to local customers. | A **car dealership** specialising solely in a wide range of second-hand electric cars. |
| A **retail shop** in a smart part of town which sells preloved designer clothes contributed entirely by its customers. | A couple with a large van packed with **food items you can buy loose;** you bring your containers and they fill them up. |
| A **holiday business** with state-of-the-art environmentally efficient cottages to rent on a site where they also offer outdoor environmental projects for kids. | A **renewable energy business** which takes the householder right through the process from assessing the current energy efficiency of a house to working out a phased programme of improvements. |
| A traditional **electrician** who has retrained to deliver a full 'smart house' service. | An **architectural practice** focusing solely on designing state-of-the-art eco-homes. |
| A **charity** providing training courses on a range of relevant skills for the future. | A **vegan ice cream stall** also selling healthy and appealing organic snacks for kids. |
| A **distribution business** using only electric vehicles to deliver locally produced food and other products. | Someone making and selling **things made from bamboo.** |
| **Recycling waste coffee** grounds into advanced biofuels and biochemicals. | **Growing crops indoors** in vertical glass 'farms'. |
| Turning non-recyclable **waste plastic into an eco-friendly replacement** for asphalt. | Kids' clothes made from **fabrics that stretch** as the child grows, meaning buying less stuff. |
| **Home-made jams,** chutneys and preserves made entirely from in-date produce discarded from supermarkets and fruit and vegetable markets. | **Edible containers** and packaging made from sustainably sourced seaweed. |
| A virtual tourism platform. | **Software** to measure the carbon footprint of major events. |

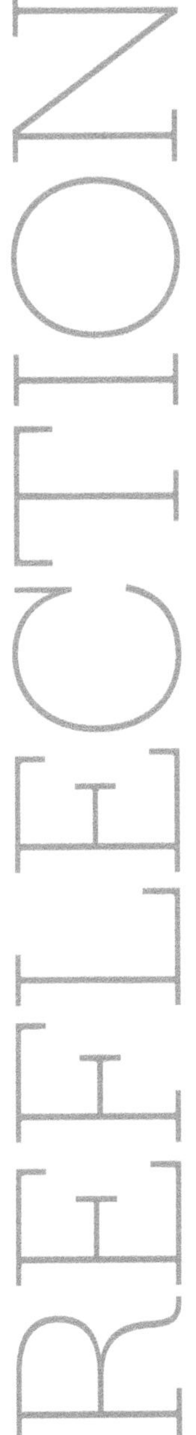


## **The thinking** How can I see myself changing my patterns of consumption and spending?

- Decarbonising holidays
- Decarbonising heating and cooling
- Decarbonising transport
- Decarbonising food
- Decarbonising energy sources
- Decarbonising events
- Decarbonising clothing
- Investment
- Carbon Compensation
- Supporting ecopreneurs

What cool spending decisions that I have already made have given me the greatest pleasure?

Any sacrifices I've made that I feel good about?

Any sacrifices I've made that I'm still struggling with?

# The action

Summarise any actions here and pencil them into your final plan as well (see pages 120–125).

CHAPTER 11

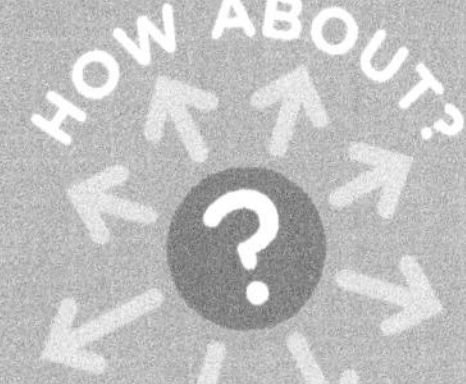


**Thinking** about low carbon footprint holidays such as walking, cycling, sailing, kayaking and swimming

INTRODUCTION

# On relevant, useful information

## Too much information

In the course of this project I have collected quite a few books on climate change. I will confess that most of them have been lightly skimmed but not read. Why? Well, I suppose it's the fact that most of them are either too long, too academic, too densely written or too full of boring lists.

If some people will go to a book for information, others will turn to the media or the internet. In talking casually to other people I find also a feeling of being overwhelmed by the explosion of media coverage. Some call it information overload.

dig deeper www.

## Short cuts

What I'm offering is to short-circuit all this, to provide you with relatively few information sources, but ones which I have found particularly useful, and/or ones which have been suggested by people I trust. But here's what's important and perhaps a bit different:

1 Instead of finding these sources in this book, you can find them on **carbonbuddyproject.org.** This ensures that this manual will stay short and uncluttered.

2 It also means that many of the sources being links to other websites, you can be reading the manual and simultaneously referencing other information on your device.

# Digging deeper

## carbonbuddyproject.org



3 The information links in the Information Gateway section of the website relate directly to each page of the manual. So it should be really quick and easy to cross-reference.

4 I have also selected a few books which I find particularly useful for their down-to-earth and practical approach (see pages 116–117).

5 If you still can't find what you want this way, then feel free to ping me an email via the website. I can't promise to answer your question myself but I'll probably be able to steer you towards someone who can.

This approach will save you a lot of time and frustration. It will give you the information you want when you want it, and in the form that is easily digestible (remember those bite-size chunks).
I hope you like it.

# The website: carbonbuddyproject.org

## Home

- How it all started
- What's The Carbon Buddy Project?
- It's their future at stake

## About

- What's the problem?
- What makes it special?

## Carbon Buddy Manual

- About the manual
- About the author
- Why a manual?
- FREE taster edition
- Reviews and comments

## Propagation

- What is a Propagator?
- Propagator's tool kit
- Ecopreneurs
- Micro-distributors

# The website: carbonbuddyproject.org

**Funding**

- My investment
- How to make it viable?
- The business model
- Your investment

**Be part of it**

- 4 ways you can help
- Sign up
- Gallery

**Events**

- Join me on the ride
- Upcoming events

**Digging deeper**

- Blog: **#mycarbonbuddy**
- The best of the books
- The Information Gateway

# People at the sharp end

Earlier in this process you will have thought about the web of people whom you know or know about, and you may well have brought some of them along with you on your ride.

You can take this further, should you wish, by **seeking out people whose work puts them at the sharp end of the challenges and opportunities** that governments, businesses, local authorities and other civil society organisations are facing in cutting carbon-based pollution.

**Watch out for these people. Ask around to find them. Take opportunities to meet and talk to them.** They are on the front line, and they need people like you to be supporting them – or nudging them!

## Look out for people who work in:

Processed food

Single use plastics

Heating, cooling

Electricity

Oil exploration

Fashion and clothing

Offshore wind energy

Retrofit of old buildings

Solar farms

Recycled clothing

Outdoor clothing manufacturers

Electricians

Low carbon travel

Independent financial advisers

Packaging materials

Coal mining

Tropical food-producing trees

Land reclamation and improvement

Agriculture in the majority world

Agribusiness

New local markets for products exported by plane

Low carbon food distribution

Energy storage

Low carbon building materials

Low carbon food production

Eliminating food waste

Electric bike specialists

Supermarkets

Recycled food

Cars and personal transport

Bicycle-related businesses

High capacity renewable energy storage

Bus operators

Cement manufacture

Carbon sequestration

Virtual tourism

Low carbon transportation

Travel and holidays

Renewable energy installers

Ecology

Waste management

Event management organisations

Air cargo

Taxi and autonomous car services

Package tour operators

Import substitution businesses

Video conferencing/ telepresence

Onshore wind energy

Passenger airlines

Rice cultivation

Market gardeners

Recycling for repurposing

Dieticians

Train companies

The re-use and repair of goods

Small scale renewable energy

Education for the green economy

Smart control systems

Local public transport

Marine biologists

Sustainable architecture

Energy assessors

Insulation contractors

Tropical forest conservation

Local spaces for start-up businesses

Growing organic food

Forestry and related industries

Slow travel

Installation of EV charging points

New skills for the future environmental economy

Plumbers

Virtual reality

Distribution

Woodland management

Outdoor clothing retailers

Working from home

Repairing things

# The best of the books

Inspirational

NO ONE IS TOO SMALL TO MAKE A DIFFERENCE
*Greta Thunberg. Penguin Random House. 2019.*

A small book of her big speeches. Clear, simple, challenging, direct, brilliant. Don't listen to her naysayers. This is dynamite, and an inspiration to us all.

Practical

**You now know about me and my obsession with bite-size chunks. I like the next three books for just that reason.** All of them are broken down into very clear and specific topics, which are well signposted. All of them are also jam-packed with practical ideas about living more sustainably whilst managing to be reasonably readable.

You'll find convenient links in the Information Gateway section of the website to order all these books.

Oh, and for the cynics and conspiracy theorists amongst you (surely not **you?**), **neither I nor the Carbon Buddy Project will get a commission from your order.**

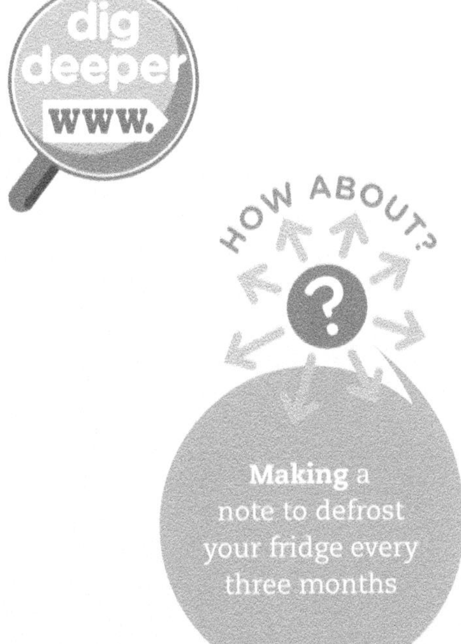


Educational

DRAWDOWN: THE MOST COMPREHENSIVE PLAN EVER PROPOSED TO REVERSE GLOBAL WARMING
*Edited by Paul Hawken. Penguin Random House. 2018.*

**The results of an awesome international multidisciplinary research project,** *Drawdown* explains how 80 ready-to-go solutions, if deployed widely, could solve the climate crisis. The presentation of each solution is informed, and above all clearly presented and illustrated. A must-go-to book if you want to understand more about the solutions in the pipeline.

### The Sustainable(ish) Living Guide

*Jen Gale. Green Tree Publishing.* 2020.

Jen Gale goes into more depth on many of the topics I have covered briefly. Although in some ways it is a book of lists, it is organised and communicated with energy and clarity and comes straight out of Jen's extensive personal experience of 'doing stuff'. Just my kind of person!

### How bad are bananas? The carbon footprint of everything

*Mike Berners-Lee. Profile Books.* 2020.

NOTE: make sure you get the new edition of this, published in 2020.

Does what it says on the tin. The go-to place to find out more about how different aspects of our lives compare regarding carbon footprints. Mike is the guru of carbon footprint science; you may have seen him on television.

### 12 small acts to save our world: YOU can make a difference

*World Wildlife Fund/Penguin Random House.* 2018.

Clearly written, and has an additional international perspective. You have to hunt in the text for the actions, but they are not too difficult to find! Inevitably has a slight slant towards wildlife issues, but covers the rest of the ground pretty well.

HOW ABOUT?

**Campaigning** to have food miles and carbon footprint of all foods shown on the label

### Zero Carbon Britain: Rising to the Climate Emergency

*CAT, Centre for Alternative Technology.* 2019.

The latest in an outstanding series of research reports which set out in detail **how the UK can reach Zero Carbon.** Aimed primarily at national and local government, and based on impeccable research by the CAT team, this report is clearly written and comprehensible, and makes a persuasive case for government action.

**Note:** There are signs that many other countries are developing their own pathways under pressure from the UN's COP (Conference of the Parties decision-making body) climate change process which is monitoring the implementation of the 2015 Paris agreement. The dramatic commitment made by China in September 2020 will add to this pressure.

CHAPTER 12

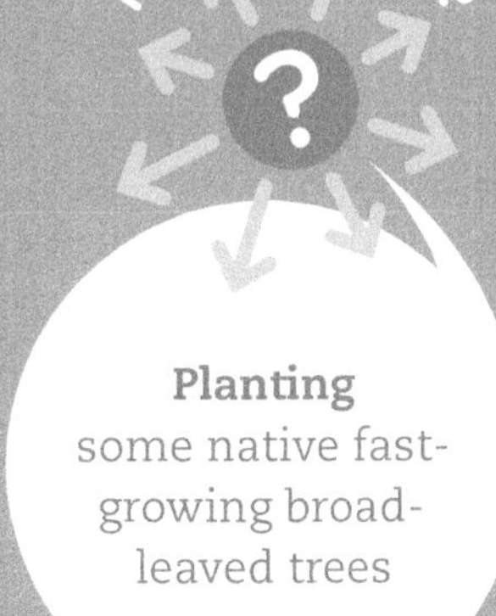

HOW ABOUT?
?
Planting
some native fast-growing broad-leaved trees


INTRODUCTION

# The Action Track: a reminder

As you have worked your way step by step through this manual, a key thread running right through it has been to come to conclusions about what practical steps you can take to reduce your personal pollution. **In my mind I have called this the Action Track.** Starting with the first conversations with your Carbon Buddy, then through to calculating your carbon footprint and identifying your biggest polluters, then to propagating, onwards to reflecting on what it means to make changes to your lifestyle, to thinking about how you can exercise your cool power and finally your cool spending choices, this will have been quite a ride. Add to that I have thrown little curved balls in from time to time in the shape of various 'nudges' to prompt you further into action.

In the next three double pages, I am providing a mechanism to bring all those action ideas together and to get an overview of what you plan to do over the next few years. **Seeing it laid out in this fashion helps you to plan realistically** to ensure you turn your good intentions into reality. But first, let me remind you about some of the key steps in the action track. You will need to go back to these pages and transfer stuff from there into your masterplan.

First conversations (pages 34–35)
Carbon footprint (pages 44–45)
Mapping priorities (pages 50–51)
Propagation (page 59)
Interlude (page 73)
Cool power (pages 84–85)
Cool ecopreneurs (pages 106–107)
Cool spending (pages 108–109)

## Tips for putting together your pollution reduction plan

- Treat yourself to a pack of mini sticky notes (50mm by 38mm). Write each action onto a sticky note and then plonk it in the appropriate box on the

# Cooling down



masterplan. The great advantage of doing it this way is that you **can change it all round easily.**

- Remember bite-size chunks? For some of the bigger, more complicated actions you'll find it helpful to break them down into a series of discrete steps spread over time. This is a good discipline to ensure you work out **what's actually involved in delivering** your nice big idea.

- If you find that too many actions are bunching up all demanding to be done at the same time, beware! **Spread them out.**

- BUT equally **beware the 'it's so difficult I'll delay it' syndrome!** The biggest, the most impactful, and the most difficult are the ones to start first. Just take small steps initially to get you going.

- Then sprinkle the shorter or easier actions amongst these more complex ones so that you can **have a feeling of making progress** on a regular basis.

- Some people are good at multi-tasking, whilst others are better doing one thing at a time. **Adapt your plan so that it works for your preferred style** of getting things done.

- You'll see that the three masterplan pages are just labelled 'short-term', 'medium-term' and 'long-term' without specifying the duration of each. Tailor these to your circumstances by filling in the timeline along the bottom in a way that works for you. But remember, **the urgency demands that 'long-term' probably needs to end by about year 5 or 6.**

- **Don't be afraid to ask for advice and help.** Finding informed people who can help you think through the decisions will save you hassle and mistakes. And it's fun too meeting such people.

- And finally, **every time you tick something off have a celebration** and go round being a pain telling everyone about what you have done.

# Summarising your plans:

## The action track

# **Short-term** pollution reduction plan

# Summarising your plans:

## The action track

# **Medium-term** pollution reduction plan

# Summarising your plans:

## The action track

# **Long-term** pollution reduction plan

# Picturing the positives

A thread has run through this manual about positivity. It's not a very fashionable idea, but I'm struck by the way that pervasive negativity about climate change can so easily drag us down into a state of helplessness or blame.

I hope that as you have worked your way through this process, from time to time you will have caught (and maybe recorded in the Seeds of Hope boxes) glimpses of how making all these changes to your lifestyle are not all about losses, but may also give rise to gains. As we did before with picturing personal pollution, I'd like to invite you to pull all these glimpses together and build them into an overall picture of the ways in which your life might actually be better in a low fossil-fuel world. Hold this in your mind when you get discouraged or depressed. It's worth hanging in there for.

# Farewell, and thank you for your companionship.

We've come to the end of our ride together. I hope you've enjoyed it as much as I have. We haven't actually reached a physical destination – because, as you will have realised, there is no final destination. **But I do hope that we may all have reached a psychological destination, in that we all now feel strong enough and confident enough to know that we can achieve our Cool Planet Goal.**

But the ride will be ongoing and will require resolve. As I've said elsewhere, the pleasure and satisfaction lie in the travelling, and in the results we achieve along the way. These will stay with us, our current young, and future generations, for ever.

COLIN HASTINGS

*November 2020*

**Do stay in touch**

I can't contact you until you contact me. So, if you feel like it, do feel free to email me. I'd love to hear from you.

colin@carbonbuddyproject.org

**#mycarbonbuddy**

carbonbuddyproject.org

Milton Keynes UK
Ingram Content Group UK Ltd.
UKHW050721060823
426322UK00002B/3